CREDO PERSPECTIVES

VOLUMES ALREADY PUBLISHED

CREDO PERSPECTIVES

PLANNED AND EDITED BY
RUTH NANDA ANSHEN

THE BRIDGE
OF LIFE

From Matter to Spirit

BY

EDMUND W. SINNOTT

SIMON AND SCHUSTER
NEW YORK 1966

CONTENTS

17850

CREDO PERSPECTIVES

Their Meaning and Function

The Credo Series suggests that twentieth-century man is living in one of the world's most challenging periods, unprecedented in history, a dynamic period when he has almost unlimited choices for good and evil. In all civilizations of the world of our modern epoch, in both socialistic and capitalistic societies, we are faced with the compelling need to understand more clearly the forces that dominate our world and to modify our attitudes and behavior accordingly. And this will only happen if our best minds are persuaded and assembled to concentrate on the nature of this new epoch in evolutionary and moral history. For we are confronted with a very basic change. Man has intervened in the evolutionary process and he must better appreciate this fact with its influence on his life and work, and then try to develop the wisdom to direct the process, to recognize the mutable and the immutable elements in his moral nature and the relationship between freedom and order.

The authors in this Series declare that science now permits us to say that "objective" nature, the world which alone is "real" to us as the one in which we all, scientists

7

included, are born, love, hate, work, reproduce and die, is the world given us by our senses and our minds—a world in which the sun crosses the sky from east to west, a world of three-dimensional space, a world of values which we, and we alone, must make. It is true that scientific knowledge about macroscopic or subatomic events may enable us to perform many acts we were unable to perform before. But it is as inhabitants of this human world that we perform them and must finally recognize that there is a certain kind of scientific "objectivity" that can lead us to know everything but to understand nothing.

The symbol of *The Credo Series* is the Eye of Osiris. It is the inner eye. Man sees in two ways: with his physical eyes, in an empirical sensing or *seeing* by direct observation, and also by an indirect envisaging. He possesses in addition to his two sensing eyes a single, image-making, spiritual and intellectual Eye. And it is the *in-sight* of this inner Eye that purifies and makes sacred our understanding of the nature of things; for that which was shut fast has been opened by the command of the inner Eye. And we become aware that to believe is to see.

This Series is designed to present a kind of intellectual autobiography of each author, to portray the nature and meaning of his creative process and to show the relevance of his work to his feelings and aspirations. In it we hope also to reflect the influence of the work on the man and on society, and to point to the freedom, or lack of freedom, to choose and pursue one profession rather than another. For the creator in any realm must surrender himself to a passionate pursuit of his labors, guided by deep personal intimations of an as yet undiscovered reality.

The Credo Series hopes to unlock a consciousness that at first sight may seem to be remote but is proved on acquaintance to be surprisingly immediate, since it stems from the need to reconcile the life of action with the life of contemplation, of practice with principle, of thought with feeling, of knowing with being. For the whole meaning of *self* lies within the observer, and its shadow is cast naturally on the object observed. The divorce of man from his work, the division of man into an eternal and temporal half, results in an estrangement of man from his creative source, and ultimately from his fellows and from himself.

The hope of this Series is to suggest that the universe itself is a vast entity where man will be lost if it does not converge in the person; for material forces or energies, or impersonal ideals, or scientifically objectified learning are meaningless without their relevance for human life and their power to disclose, even in the dark tendencies of man's nature, a law transcending man's arbitrariness.

For the personal is a far higher category than the abstract universal. Personality itself is an emotional, not an intellectual, experience; and the greatest achievement of knowledge is to combine the personal within a larger unity, just as in the higher stages of development the parts that make up the whole acquire greater and greater independence and individuality within the context of the whole. Reality itself is the harmony which gives to the component particulars of a thing the equilibrium of the whole. And while physical observations are ordered with direct reference to the experimental conditions, we have in sensate experience to do with separate observations whose correlation can only be indicated by their belonging to the wholeness of mind.

It is the endeavor of the authors to show that man has reached a turning point in consciousness, that his relationship with his creativity demands a clarification that can widen and deepen his understanding of the nature of reality. Work is made for man, not man for work. This Series hopes to demonstrate the sacramental character of work, which is more easily achieved when the principal objects of our attention have taken on a symbolic form that is generally recognized and accepted; and this suggests a *law* in the relationship of a person and his chosen discipline: that it is valuable only when the spiritual, the creative, life is strong enough to insist on some expression through symbols. For no work can be based on material, technological, historical, or physical aspirations alone.

The human race is now entering upon a new phase of evolutionary consciousness and progress, a phase in which, impelled by the forces of evolution itself, it must converge upon itself and convert itself into one single human organism infused by a reconciliation of knowing and being in their inner unity and destined to make a qualitative leap into a higher form of consciousness that would transcend and complement individual consciousness as we know it, or otherwise destroy itself. For the entire universe is one vast field, potential for incarnation and achieving incandescence here and there of reason and spirit. And in the whole world of *quality* with which by the nature of our minds we necessarily make contact, we here and there apprehend pre-eminent value. This can be achieved only if we recognize that we are unable to focus our attention on the particulars of a whole without diminishing our comprehension of the whole, and of course, conversely, we can focus on the whole only by diminishing our comprehension of the particulars which constitute the whole.

The kind of knowledge afforded by mathematical physics ever since the seventeenth century has come more and more to furnish mankind with an ideal for all knowledge. This error about the nature of knowledge it is the hope of this Series to expose. For knowledge is a process, not a product and the results of scientific investigation do not carry with them self-evident implications. There are now, however, signs of new centers of resistance among men everywhere in almost all realms of knowledge. Many share the conviction that a deep-seated moral and philosophical reform is needed concerning our understanding of the nature of man and the nature of knowledge in relation to the work man is performing, in relation to his *credo* and his life.

The Credo Series constitutes an endeavor to alter the prevailing conceptions, not only of the nature of knowledge and work, but also of creative achievements in general, as well as of the human agent who inquires and creates, and of the entire fabric of the culture formed by such activities. In other words, this is an endeavor to show that what we see and what we do are no more and no less than what we are.

It is the endeavor of *The Credo Series* to define the new reality in which the estrangement of man from his work, resulting in the self-estrangement in man's existence, is overcome. This new reality is born through the reconciliation of what a man *knows* with what a man *is*. Being itself in all its presuppositions and implications can only be understood through the totality, through wholeness. St. Paul, who, like Isaiah before him, went into the market-place not to secularize truth but to proclaim it, taught man that the "new creation" could be explained only by con-quering the daemonic cleavages, the destructive split, in soul and cosmos. And that fragmentation always destroys a unity, produces a tearing away from the source and thereby creates disunity and isolation. The fruit can never be separated from the tree. The Tree of Life can never be disjoined from the Tree of Knowledge for both have *one and the same* root. And if man allows himself to fall into isolation, if he seeks to maintain a self segregated from the totality of which he is a necessary part, if he chooses to be unrelated to the original context of all created things in which he too has his place—including his own labors— then this act of apostasy bears fruit in the demiurgical pre-sumption of *magic,* a form of animism in which man seeks an authority of the self, placing himself above the law of the universe by attempting to separate the inseparable. He thus creates an unreal world after having destroyed or de-serted the real. And in this way the method of analysis, of scientific objectivity, which is good and necessary in its right place, is endowed with a destructive power when it is allowed to usurp a place for which it is not fitted.

The naturalist principle that man is the measure of all things has been shattered more than ever in our own age by the question, "What is the measure of man?" Post-modern man is more profoundly perplexed about the na-ture of man than his ancestors were. He is on the verge of spiritual and moral insanity. He does not know who he is.

And having lost the sense of who and what he is, he fails to grasp the meaning of his fellow man, of his vocation and of the nature and purpose of knowledge itself. For what is not understood cannot be known. And it is this cognitive faculty which is frequently abrogated by the "scientific" theory of knowledge, a theory that refuses to recognize the existence of comprehensive entities as distinct from their particulars. The central act of knowing is indeed that form of comprehension which is never absent from any process of knowing and is finally its ultimate sanction.

Science itself acknowledges as real a host of entities that cannot be described completely in materialistic or mechanistic terms, and it is this transcendence out of the domain of science into a region from which science itself can be appraised that *The Credo Series* hopes to define. For the essence of the ebb and flow of experience, of sensations, the richness of the immediacy of directly apprehended knowledge, the metaphysical substance of what assails our being, is the very act itself of sensation and affection and therefore must escape the net of rational analysis, yet is intimately related to every cognitive act. It is this increasing intellectual climate that is calling into birth once more the compelling Socratic questions, "What is the purpose of life, the meaning of work?" "What is man?" Plato himself could give us only an indirect answer: "Man is declared to be that creature who is constantly in search of himself, a creature who at every moment of his existence must examine and scrutinize the conditions of his existence. He is a being in search of meaning."

From this it is evident that there is present in the universe a *law* applicable to all nature including man and his work. Life itself then is seen to be a creative process elaborating and maintaining *order* out of the randomness of matter, endlessly generating new and unexpected structures and properties by building up associations that qualitatively transcend their constituent parts. This is not to diminish the importance of "scientific objectivity." It is, however, to say that the mind possesses a quality that cannot be isolated or known exclusively in the sense of objective knowledge. For it consists in that elusive humanity in us, our self, that knows. It is that inarticulate awareness that includes and *comprehends* all we know. It consists in the irreducible active voice of man and is recognized only in other things, only when the circle of consciousness closes around its universe of events.

Our hope is to point to a new dimension of morality— not that of constraint and prohibition but a morality that lies as a fountainhead within the human soul, a morality of aspiration to spiritual experience. It suggests that necessity is laid upon us to infer entities that are not observed and are not observable. For an unseen universe is necessary to explain the seen. The flux is seen, but to account for its structure and its nature we infer particles of various kinds to serve as the vertices of the changing patterns, placing less emphasis on the isolated units and more on the structure and nature of relations. The process of knowing involves an immaterial becoming, an immaterial identification, and finally, knowledge itself is seen to be a dependent variable of immateriality. And somewhere along this spiritual pilgrimage man's pure observation is relinquished and gives way to the deeper experience of awe, for there can be no explanation of a phenomenon by searching for its origin but only by discerning its immanent law—this quality of transcendence that abides even in matter itself. The present situation in the world and the vast accretion of knowledge have produced a serious anxiety which may be overcome by re-evaluating the character, kinship, logic and operation of man in relation to his work. For work implies goals and intimately affects the person performing the work. Therefore the correlation and relatedness of ideas, facts and values that are in perpetual interplay could emerge from these volumes as they point to the inner synthesis and organic unity of man and his labors. For though no labor alone can enrich the person, no enrichment can be achieved without absorbing and intense labor. We then experience a unity of faith, labor and grace which prepares the mind for receiving a truth from sources over which it has no control. This is especially true since the great challenge of our age arises out of man's inventions in relation to his life.

Thus *The Credo Series* seeks to encourage the perfection not only of man's works but also and above all the fulfillment of himself as a person. And so we now are summoned to consider not only man in the process of development as a human subject but also his influence on the object of his investigation and creation. Observation alone is interference. The naïve view that we can observe any system and predict its behavior without altering it by the very act of observation was an unjustified extrapolation from Newton's *Celestial Mechanics*. We can observe the moon or even a satellite and predict its behavior without perhaps appreciably interfering with it, but we cannot do this with an amoeba, far less with a man and still less with a society of men. It is the heart of the question of the nature of work itself. If we regard our labors as a process of shaping or forming, then the fruits of our labors play the part of a mold by which we ourselves are shaped. And this means, in the preservation of the identity of the knower and the known, that cognition and generation, that is, creation, though in different spheres, are nevertheless alike.

It is hoped that the influence of such a Series may help to overcome the serious separations between function and meaning and may show that the extraordinary crisis through which the world is passing can be fruitfully met by recognizing that knowledge has not been completely dehumanized and has not totally degenerated into a mere notebook overcrowded with formulas that few are able to understand or apply.

For mankind is now engaged in composing a new theme. Life never manifests itself in negative terms. And our hope lies in drawing from every category of work a conviction that nonmaterial values can be discovered in positive, affirmative, visible things. The estrangement between the temporal and nontemporal man is coming to an end, community is inviting communion, and a vision of the human condition more worthy of man is engendered, connecting ever more closely the creative mind with the currents of spiritual energy which breaks for us the bonds of habit and keeps us in touch with the permanence of being through our work.

And as, long ago, the Bearers of Bread were succeeded by the Bearers of Torches, so now, in the immediacies of life, it is the image of man and his vocation that can rekindle the high passion of humanity in its quest for light.

Refusing to divorce work from life or love from knowledge, it is action, it is passion that enhances our being.

We live in an expanding universe and also in the moral infinite of that other universe, the universe of man. And along the whole stretched arc of this universe we may see that extreme limit of complicity where reality seems to shape itself within the work man has chosen for his realization. Work then becomes not only a way of knowledge, it becomes even more a way of life—of life in its totality. For the last end of every maker is himself.

"And the places that have been desolate for ages shall be built in thee: thou shalt raise up the foundations of generation and generation; and thou shalt be called the repairer of the fences, turning the paths into rest."*

—RUTH NANDA ANSHEN

---

* Isaiah, 58:12.

MY CREDO

What makes a man a biologist—aside from the fact that he likes to work with living things—is the conviction that life presents the most important and most difficult problems that man faces. Life is closely involved in the universal questions of food and sex and race that shake the world today. Beyond these, it touches the deeper questions of what life is, and thus of what man is—body, soul and spirit. The problems of philosophy and even of religion are, in essence, problems of *life,* and thus in the domain of the biologist in the broadest sense of this word. It was a recognition of this inclusive and fundamental quality of life that persuaded me to become a biologist rather than a physicist or a psychologist or a sociologist.

No scientist, at the start of his career, lays it out as a single piece, already planned and waiting only its accomplishment. Rather does he "play it by ear," so to speak, following his various urgencies and taking advantage of the opportunities with which he is presented. There is rarely a clear insight, at the start, of what his course will be. The development of a biologist, for example, is like that of any organism he studies. It is a gradual unfolding, each step conditioned by the one before it and by his native quality, his experience and the environment in which he lives. This ontogenetic character of a man's life is what makes biography such a fascinating subject. As this *Credo Series* of volumes shows so well, the developmental study of a scholar or a man of science illuminates his life more clearly than does a merely chronological listing of his deeds, ideas, and conclusions.

I began as a student of plants, which are among the simplest of living things and are hardly recognized by some people as being actually alive. For a long time I collected them in the field, reveling in their great diversity and beautiful adaptations to their surroundings. My next step, as in the history of botany itself, was to help classify this great variety of organisms into a system based on their evolutionary relationships. Darwin was the first to point out that the traits most important in determining these relationships are the ones of *form*. For this reason and also, perhaps, because of the innate attractiveness to me of organic forms, I soon became a plant morphologist, not simply describing plant forms but comparing them with one another and thus trying to determine the evolutionary pathways by which they had arisen.

Forms are constant and specific and are transmitted from one generation to the next, and I soon became interested in their inheritance, in the physical means by which the traits of parents are transmitted to their offspring. Genetics was developing at this time, and many biologists felt that it would solve the ultimate problems of their science. I therefore began to study the genetics of form, using for this purpose the shape of the fruits in the Cucurbitaceae, the family to which the squashes, gourds and pumpkins belong. It soon became clear that these characters of form were determined by genes and followed, in their inheritance, the laws of Mendel. Out of this work grew studies in the genetics of other structural differences.

I soon saw that much can be learned about organic form by studying the way in which it develops, especially under a variety of conditions. Discoveries in this field, the science of morphogenesis or experimental development, impressed me in my earlier years with the fact that a living thing, be it plant or animal, is an organized system in which each part or process is related to the others. As I studied the development of various plant structures and read of the work that experimental embryologists had done on animals, I became convinced—and the conviction has never left me —that the presence of this biological organization is the most distinctive feature of all life. Form itself is the visible expression of it. The recent great advances in biochemical genetics have tended to obscure this fact and to focus attention primarily upon the individual genes and their composition. But the organism is more than a collection of genes. It is bound together as a unit. In every cell of an individual there seems to be something that represents the organized system as a whole, for every cell has the potentiality of reproducing the individual if conditions are favorable. This "something" is apparently an inherent norm or pattern to which development, from fertilized egg to adult, tends to move. Merely to identify the chemical character of each gene does not explain the way in which thousands of genes are so integrated that an organized whole, an *organism,* is produced. The claim of some geneticists today that biology itself is nothing more, ultimately, than the study of the nucleic acids (the materials of which genes are made) is therefore, in my opinion, far too narrow a view, for it omits the most important quality of life.

I have been impressed more and more, as the years went on, with this fact of organization, and it underlies the next step in the development of the ideas in biological philosophy which I have proposed in several books and amplified in the present one; ideas that are not concerned with plants and animals alone but have expanded to include man himself. The unity of life must impress itself on every thoughtful biologist. Protoplasm is very constant in character wherever we find it, and genes are chemically much the same in the simplest plants as they are in man. The complexities of life as we find it in the higher animals, and especially in man, are complexities of behavior and lead to phenomena usually called mental or psychological. To try to interpret these in biological terms I made the suggestion some years ago that what is commonly called a purpose or a goal, or an ideal (psychical qualities) toward the realization of which behavior is oriented, is the same *sort* of thing as the norm toward which bodily development is oriented, but that, unlike the latter, it is subjectively experienced. If there is any important contribution I have made to biological philosophy, it perhaps is the emphasis given to this suggestion, though many biologists and philosophers question its validity and maintain that it is really nothing, at last, but the sort of mysticism with which a scientist should not concern himself.

In my own defense, I should like to point out that the most important problem that biological philosophy must face is the relation of the psychical to the physical, the ancient mind-body issue. My position, set forth elsewhere and in detail in the present book, points to the similarity in several respects between the developmental pattern of the body of an organism and the behavioral pattern it displays. This does not prove that mental and developmental phenomena are the same, nor does it explain one by the other, but it suggests that they have a common protoplasmic basis. There obviously must be a relation between the physical basis of the brain and the behavioral controls, subjectively experienced, that are based in it. My suggestion may not be the correct one to explain the body-mind relationship, but it is defensible and deserves more consideration than to be brushed aside as merely visionary.

With this idea as a basis, I began to consider other philosophical questions usually shunned by biologists as outside the domain of science. On the concept of biological organization may be based an interpretation not only of mind but of what are called the soul and the human spirit. To maintain, as many do, that such things are nonexistent and therefore not worth a scientist's attention is to hold, it seems to me, altogether too narrow an idea of man's nature. He is a far more complex creature than we usually give him credit for being, and to take the orthodox mechanistic view of him is to shut one's eyes to much of what he is and what he may become. Even the idea of God may be related to that of the organization of life. Tennyson's lines on the "flower in the crannied wall" have far more than simply a poetic significance.

Half-baked and indefensible ideas have often been proposed by men of science but this does not mean that

philosophy has no deep roots in science or that a man of
science should not feel free to discuss them even if he has
no union card as a philosopher. Biology is especially important in these problems. The distance between matter
and man is so very great that to develop a purely mechanistic theory of what he is seems quite impossible; but it
is possible, I believe, on the basis of a knowledge of the
attributes of life and particularly of its organizing relations,
to come to an interpretation of the higher attributes of
man—his psychological traits—that is helpful in understanding him. At a lower and purely biological level, it
should also be possible to understand how these distinctive
qualities of life have a physical basis. If biologists can discover what this is, the way will be clear, I think, to relate
man's highest qualities to his material ones by way of his
biological character and thus to help find his true place in
the universe. The most immediately important steps in the
problem are therefore to be made by the biologist in discovering the true nature of *life* rather than by a philosopher
who limits himself to a study of the nature of man alone.
Life is truly, I believe, a bridge between the purely material universe and those higher aspects of it which a study
of man discloses. It is this idea of life as a bridge which
I have tried to develop in the present book.

The author's journey has now progressed by one more
stage. The parlous state of the world today and the im-
minent danger of the destruction of all man's values must
be in the mind of every scientist. What contribution he can
make to the prevention of this holocaust should be his chief
concern. It has seemed to me, particularly in the past few
years, that what is chiefly needed to this end is not so much

a better organization of the nations for peace, or the spread
of freedom, or the abolition of race hatreds or any other
specific remedy, but rather the development and dissemi-
nation of a philosophy of life that can be shared by everyone. Only thus can men finally be united. About this goal
the scientist and the philosopher should both have much
to say. There are two major contenders here for the allegiance of man. They are commonly termed *materialism*
and *religion*. The issue between them is not unlike the one
between men who believe that life involves only a rigid
physical determinism and those who see in life and its
relation to the universe something beyond this, something
to which the phenomenon of biological organization may
perhaps give a clue. It has seemed to me that the interpretation of life that I have tried to develop here may perhaps
serve as a basis on which these contending philosophies
could finally come more closely together and which thus
might serve to promote harmony among men. It was in
the hope of accomplishing this that the present book was
written.

To come to such conclusions as these has required a
long odyssey indeed from the early work of a young bota-
nist who published a paper on the pond flora of Cape Cod,
describing the species and distribution of the plants found
along the shores of the many lakes and ponds on that
delightful peninsula. This work, however, was concerned
with an aspect, albeit a simple one, of the character of
life. The papers and books I have published in the half-
century since that time have also had life as their theme,
but life at progressively higher levels. The conclusions that
grew out of this work may have little appeal to many

readers and will be vigorously opposed by others. This introductory discussion of it may also seem to be unduly self-centered, but one should remember that the primary purpose of the present series of books is to describe the stages in the development of a person's scholarly and scientific life, the evolution of his ideas. These stages in my own case are sketched in this CREDO. Their details are more fully elaborated in the text itself. It is my modest hope that this book may help to guide those in search of knowledge of the meaning and purpose of life.

I

TOWARD A COMMON LIFE
PHILOSOPHY

It is written that when the descendants of the sons of Noah moved westward from the Assyrian hills and down into the broad plain of Shinar, they were seized with one of those grandiose ambitions that from time to time through history have stirred the hearts of men. They resolved to build a great tower there that would reach toward heaven itself. Perhaps what made them try to raise this man-made hill was a longing for the ones that they had left behind, just as a monarch near this spot, centuries later, built hanging gardens for his homesick queen. Perhaps it was to gain a lofty post from which better to observe the movements of the heavenly bodies, of much concern to men who live under a wide sky. Whatever its cause, the undertaking was vigorously begun. It must have required for its accomplishment workmen more numerous than that little company of the offspring of Shem, Ham and Japheth. Doubtless people from surrounding tribes and with somewhat different speech and ways of thinking were called upon to help put up the great stepsided ziggurat. This caused, I think, the discord and confusion that finally put an end to the building of the tower of Babel. The workmen were not able to communicate with one another well enough, or to agree about the grand design to which they had put their hands. In the end the sons of Noah had to abandon their ambitious plan, and once more became wanderers across the plain.

From that day to our own, the most far-seeing men have dreamed that this age-old confusion might be ended and that people everywhere would learn to live in friendship and in mutual understanding. Whenever serious attempts were made to realize these dreams, however, man's selfishness and ignorance and obstinacy finally prevented their fulfillment. Even in our own enlightened day, these blocks to human unity are still effective, so that the unhappy history of Babel's tower is being repeated in the great edifice of civilization man is building now. Never before has he achieved such confident mastery over nature, never built so high nor looked toward such a wide horizon. Today he molds the earth to his desires. He moves almost at will on land and sea and through the pathways of the air, and he aspires to vaster conquests in the limitless realms of space. Nevertheless, within this mighty fabric can be seen the forces of disruption that led to the abandonment of the great tower long ago. Differences in political and economic systems seriously divide mankind. Across wide frontiers, nations are snarling at one another. Racial hatred is violent, crime is increasing, and war is still a means of settling disputes.

These problems men long have known and tried to solve, but to them now are added even graver ones, outgrowths of the rapid advance of science in the past few decades. Machines have taken over much of what men used to do, so that many hands are idle. Society has grown so vulnerable in its vast complexity that even a minor dislocation threatens to bring disaster. Surfeit stands side by side with famine. Populations are exploding and resources dwindling, as the ghost of Malthus rises to haunt mankind. These are troubles that our fathers never had. Crises in earlier days were localized by distance. What happened on the far-off plains of Muscovy touched us but little, and Europe was weeks from America by sail; but today we are deprived of the leisurely perspective that such distance gave, the cushioning effect of space. Our planet is so shrunken now that men from its far corners can assemble in a day, and an army flies the Atlantic between dawn and dark. Those in the uttermost parts of the earth listen to news from everywhere, and even see it made. In such a close-knit world, friendship and peace do not grow automatically. A little flame of hate can start a conflagration, and such flames are burning now. Dissensions divide us so deeply as to threaten the very survival of our species, for hanging over all, like the great sword of Damocles, is the threat of a nuclear holocaust. Never before has it been possible, as now it is, to blot out the human race in half an hour. There are no more open spaces to which we can flee, no frontiers beyond which we are safe. The plain fact is that for the first time in history, large-scale war as a means of settling disputes has become impossible. If someone dares invoke it, or a desperate Hitler should unloose the monster from his lair within the atom, all three billion of us would meet an awful fate. To stave off such a catastrophe we desperately appeal to the balance of power, or the balance of terror, or some clever diplomatic maneuver, but we know there are no final answers there. Man cannot live long under this awful threat. He cannot wait, shivering and apprehensive, from week to week, in dread of the great mushroom clouds that mean his doom. He tries not to think of them, but they are still the background of his life. It is not strange that as he looks into the future he is frightened and discouraged. The most hopeful fact today is that men are coming to realize that some other means than force must be used to settle the differences and antagonisms that inevitably arise among them.

The time for drastic action now is here. If man is to survive, he must deliberately and vigorously bring to pass what he so long has dreamed of—the brotherhood of man. If he indeed is *Homo sapiens,* the day has come when he must justify this proud binomial or stumble into well-deserved disaster. The unity of the human race is what must be achieved. It is good and pleasant, as the Psalmist said, for brothers to dwell together in unity. In the past this was a high ideal, but it has now become a sheer necessity. The very pressure of our time is forcing us to choose between unity and disaster. All ages in man's history have been dangerous ones, but in every field of life the dangers are more grave today than they have ever been.

How this unity may be accomplished has been the subject of much thought and effort. The most tangible result is the organization of the United Nations, but the United States of Europe, "One World," and other ideas have been widely discussed. Most of these were to be based on political union or at least on joint political action, but the difficulties inherent in such a plan became evident with the years. To bind us together, I believe, there must be something deeper than political institutions, or economic systems, or race or language. It must involve man's basic *beliefs,* the *philosophy* by which he tries to shape his life, the things in which he puts his *faith.* We must reach greater agreement on our fundamental assumptions. This is far harder to achieve than mere political unity but without it progress will be very slow. Many thoughtful men have come to this conclusion. "If our times are out of joint," says Overstreet, "it is because they are philosophically out of joint. If we are to set them right we shall have to set them philosophically right." Von Ogden Vogt agrees. Says, "A nation must make up its mind before it can make its morals. . . . We cannot progress much farther without a thoroughgoing review as to what our philosophy is." Lancelot Whyte puts it more strongly: "Without some universally accepted ideas about nature and man there can be no stable world order. . . . Today the only hope of social order lies in the establishment of a valid universalism." René Dubos, lamenting the decadence of much modern life, says that to correct it, "common action cannot be mustered, because it would demand a common faith that does not exist."

Differences in their beliefs have set men at their neighbors' throats across the centuries. These are the most deeply seated disagreements that divide us and the hardest to reconcile because they comprise the very core of what a person is, the place where he comes to grips with reality. If our differences all were intellectual ones they would not be so difficult to resolve, but they go much deeper and

reach the wellsprings of emotion. To serve as a unifying
force a common faith must recognize this and provide a
deeper basis for unity than a purely rational one. It must
accept the fact that in his real nature a man is not only a
material and a rational being but a spiritual one as well.
Brotherhood means not simply agreeing with your neighb
but treating him as though he were your *brother*. It ha
warmth of feeling in it. To reach this means a change
human relationships so radical that we can hardly im
how it may be brought to pass. Nevertheless, this c
or a substantial approach toward its accomplishm
the price that we must pay to be freed from the inc
that bears so heavily upon us now and prevents our m
freely toward the happy future of which we used to
confident.

What I am suggesting, in short, is that *true peace
happiness on earth, the unity and brotherhood of mank
will not be achieved until men reach agreement as to
basic religious philosophy by which they try to live.*
problem is as simple—and as difficult—as this.

By "religious" I do not mean necessarily related to
church or a creed or a ritual, but having a deep conce
for fundamentals, a reverence for something that tra
scends material things. Even from this interpretation mar
will dissent. Religion, they believe, is no sound basis f
an intelligent philosophy since it introduces concepts o
mysticism, idealism, the spirit and other immaterial elements that are opposed to the conclusions of science and
thus must be untrue. This attitude recalls those simpler
days when men were much more sure than they are now of
what truth is. Even the truth about matter we are still far

from comprehending. Life, despite the great discoveries
about it, remains still more of an enigma. And as to man,
whom we persist in trying to reduce to a chemical machine,
we fail to recognize how vastly more complex he is than
this. Whence come his values, aspirations and other spiritual qualities we do not know, but we cannot fail to take
these into account if we are to probe the depths of the
problems he presents and build for him a satisfying philosophy of life. The time is past when, in our pride of
intellect, we can arbitrarily rule out as valueless *any* vital
part of human experience, by whatever name it may be
called. Science is man's attempt to gain an intellectual
understanding of the material universe and is of great significance for his philosophy; but religion seeks to under-
pin and those qualities that are immaterial. These also are
of much importance for human life and may be disregarded
at our peril.

Man seeks answers to some very searching questions.
What is his place and significance in this unimaginably vast
system of the universe, seemingly infinite and eternal?
Within it is he anything more than a bundle of matter,
moved about by the energy that is matter's other face,
caught up in the toils of a destiny as meaningless as it is
inescapable? Is there room in it for immaterial things, for
the high values he calls beauty, goodness, truth? We know
how difficult these questions are and what momentous consequences follow from the answers to them that we give.
The philosophy that helps a man reply to them, whether
it is called a religious one or not, is the most distinctive
thing about him.

Despite what scoffers say, religion of some sort, some

coming to terms with the universe, is a necessity for everyone. When man emerged as a rational being, "a stranger
and afraid, in a world he never made," the weight of doubt
and fear that must have oppressed him would have been
unbearable had he not been reassured by some primitive
faith. We have not outgrown this need today. Each of us
must find his own way to meet the challenges that confront
us. To do this, some men have identified themselves with
one or another of the numberless systems of organized
religion. Others abandon all formal religion and subscribe
to humanism, agnosticism or atheism. Still others, standing
aloof from any philosophical commitment, have set up in
their hearts some private hypothesis on which to stake their
lives. Too often they are scornful of one another's faiths
and isolate themselves in dogmatism. Many discredit religion altogether as blind superstition. This chaos of beliefs
touches all other differences among men. To remedy the
confusion of our modern Babel no superficial palliatives
will be enough; no improved social organization, no fired-
up education, no new techniques for amity among the nations. These will be useful but they do not pierce to the
deep root of the difficulty. We must *agree* before we can
unite. If the universe is truly a consistent unity, then inso-
far as we can reach an understanding of it, our beliefs
about it should approach a unity as well.

But the possibility that men can gain such unity now
seems so remote that many will regard a serious attempt
to reach it as unrealistic and even preposterous. If we have
learned anything about the members of our race it is that
they are notorious for disagreeing with one another, and
in matters of religion most of all. Some of the bloodiest

wars in history have been fought not for glory or empire but to force on others the acceptance of a particular faith. What hope is there, we ask, that men could be persuaded *now* to give up their cherished beliefs and accept some other philosophy? So many more hopeful enterprises seek our help that many would say we ought not to waste energy on a desperate venture such as this.

Apart from the general hopelessness of the project, serious objections to it may be raised. Some people will regard the goal itself as actually *un*desirable, and maintain that a common belief would not only take the flavor of diversity out of life but end all hope of change and progress. Differences stimulate new ideas, on which the advancing course of man depends. There is merit in this objection, for without diversity life would surely stagnate. Men are so different, however, in their natural gifts and their proclivities that it is impossible to fit them into any single mold, and the boredom of uniformity is the least danger that we have to fear. Ample opportunity would exist for wide divergence of ideas, though still within the framework of a general agreement. It is only the fundamental differences that need to be resolved.

But, granted the desirability of a common faith, it will be very difficult to discover the truth on which to base it. Truth, about which we once could feel so sure, today is often very hard to find. Axioms have lost their old authority. Natural law is based on probability. Truth, like so many other things, may turn out to be a relative, not an absolute, thing. It is many-sided and can be reached by different roads. One may object that a philosophy about it that is satisfactory to one man may not be so to another, and that a variety of faiths, or none at all, may in the end contribute more to human welfare than can any single, monolithic system of belief. To the great majority of folk, however, the idea that truth thus is multiple has little attraction, and they are inclined to leave the fine-spun speculations about such matters to professional philosophers. The great faith of science, where this issue can be joined most closely, is that truth *does* exist and that it *can* be discovered. Without this faith science would be meaningless. Complete certainty on many questions is impossible, but a mature mind learns to do without it. All people, of course, will not think alike, for each man must approach the truth in his own way and grow into a clearer understanding of it. The general climate of opinion changes, too, and the heterodoxies of one generation often become the orthodoxies of another. But this does not mean that truth should not be sought or cannot be found. To give up the pursuit of it, to which he has for so long been devoted, would be to declare man's intellectual and spiritual bankruptcy.

Another objection to the proposal is the very great difficulty of bringing it to pass. It would be almost as hard to accomplish as to lead the rivers of a continent together and make them run in a single channel to the sea. Although the great religions of the world, however, do have many differences, they also have many things in common. It is conceivable that in time something like an Ecumenical Council of Protestants, Roman Catholics, Jews, Mohammedans, Hindus and Buddhists might be gathered that would emphasize and clarify these similarities. The suggested "Temple of Understanding" in Washington could well be a focal point for this objective. Nevertheless, there are stubborn differences among the great religious faiths which it would be hard to reconcile; and if it is difficult to unite these, that have in common a recognition of spiritual elements in the universe and man, how much harder it would be to bring in with them the legions of those who have no faith at all. Surely, one may say, there is no common denominator that all these men can share.

Even though an optimist, trusting in the ultimate triumph of human reason, is still confident that all men can reach, in time, some common understanding as to their basic philosophies, there remain very serious practical difficulties. Obviously such an agreement requires patient and friendly consideration of the issues. Save under special circumstances, such conferences are hard to bring about. In these enlightened days it seems strange that men should so often be unwilling to face free discussion of questions which to them are—or should be—of the utmost final concern; but such, alas, is the case. A man's religion, many feel, is his private affair, and tinkering with it should never be allowed. Proselyting is generally frowned upon, save to convert the "heathen." Ecclesiastical bodies are notoriously sensitive to attempts to change the minds of their adherents, and we know the impossibility, in a Communist state, of successfully challenging the party line. In the press and other media there is often a taboo against discussing matters of faith because of the bitterness that may be engendered. The long and often bloody history of religious quarrels makes men hesitate to fan again their embers into flame.

Even with free discussion, the possibility of changing the

minds of most people as to their fundamental beliefs is slight. A man generally adopts the religious philosophy in which he was brought up, and from this source come the beliefs he tends most firmly to maintain. Many of these are demonstrably untrue, and one might expect that in a general enlightenment they would be cast aside; but so prejudiced is the attitude of many people still that progress will be slow indeed. A man will often hold to his faith—or lack of it—with such a rigid and determined dogmatism that his ears are closed to all opposing arguments. Someone has said that the tenacity with which one maintains a belief is *inversely* proportional to its credibility. Such dogmatism is by no means universal but it is common enough to be a serious block to constructive discussion of fundamental questions, to free flow of the traffic in ideas. The judicial temperament is not a common human attribute. In any matter where opinion is divided, man is notoriously prone to take sides vigorously, to be an advocate and not a neutral judge. This in the past has been a useful trait, for without it he never could have nourished the enthusiasms, convictions and devotions that were necessary in the building of a society, but often is a handicap today.

The greatest practical difficulty of all in bringing to pass what has been suggested here comes from the heavy inertial drag of human indifference. In an age as secular as ours, why worry about religion, one may ask? Theological disputation should be left to philosophers and clergymen. What a man *believes* is really not very important, anyway. It is what he *does* that counts. This is a common attitude. Even the Bible says that pure religion is to visit the fatherless and widows in their affliction, and keep one's self unspotted from the world. Many issues, indeed, seem of more pressing interest than one's personal philosophy. Today, as always, man tends to be more concerned with material than with immaterial things, with the immediate and necessary problems of his life. In the background of his mind, however, there still persist those deeper questions that confront him as a rational being. If now he loses his concern for them and pretends that they are not important, he is less by that much than the full stature of the man he ought to be.

A final objection to our proposal is that the unity of mankind will not come through the development of a common religious philosophy but from the growth of a feeling of brotherhood, a real *love* for our neighbors. If this is gained, all else will follow. It requires, say its proponents, no program of philosophic argument and persuasion but an outpouring of the spirit, a great missionary enterprise to bring the hearts of men together. This, indeed, must be our final aim, but the very serious difficulties in bringing it to pass are obvious. It will be easier, I am sure, to be a friend to someone whose mind goes along with ours than to one with whom we disagree on fundamental matters. Agreement is the first step toward affection, and brotherhood involves them both.

Such are some of the difficulties and objections that must be met in trying to reach a life philosophy that all men can share. Though the chances for success seem very slender, failure would finally have consequences so disastrous that we should not abandon our efforts through sheer hopelessness. Actually, the prospects of gaining such a goal as this, desperate though they may seem to be, are brighter,

I believe, than in the past. Men are better educated and
think for themselves more often. Ignorance and prejudice,
to be sure, are everywhere and have deep roots but not
so deep as they were a century ago. Men would not fight a
Thirty Years' War again, and many of the quarrels of the
past are looked upon today as childish ones. The task is
not as formidable as it might seem at first, for it is not the
whole population that would have to be persuaded but only
its intellectual leadership, its opinion-makers, whose influence is great. I do not underestimate the very serious
difficulty of gaining their support for the cause of philosophical agreement, but at least they are open to rational
argument. How powerful such a minority can be is shown
by the history of the idea of organic evolution. Before
this gained strong support from Darwin's theory of natural
selection, almost everyone was opposed to it, for it seemed
to deny the very foundations of Christianity; but it was
soon accepted by many intellectuals and gradually won
over almost all whose opinion commands respect. For
many people this involved as drastic changes in their attitude toward religion as the ones to be proposed here,
but it is now successfully accomplished and has left few
scars. Since science is so highly esteemed today, the way
in which its practitioners promptly give up long established
theories as soon as new evidence proves these to be in-
correct has been a notable example of the worthlessness of
dogmatism. Indeed, the scientific community itself is a
powerful influence for open-mindedness and rational belief. It shows that in some important respects people *do*
change their minds. I believe that the task of changing
them still further, to the point where they can reach essen-

tial agreement as to their fundamental faiths, is not the completely hopeless undertaking it might seem to be, and that it has a reasonable chance of ultimate success. To achieve this is man's most pressing responsibility today. No civilization that has reached maturity should be daunted by the challenge.

Though differences among us still are great, the points on which intelligent folk agree are so many that if we tried earnestly we could go far toward accomplishing the unity we seek. One great step would be to gain tolerance for the beliefs of others and to recognize that they may be able to see a part of the truth which we have not yet found. At least it should be possible for thoughtful people to avoid the violent dogmatisms that so often have bedeviled religious disputations in the past. We can also reach fairly general agreement, I am sure, that a host of ideas and beliefs, among them some ancient and deep-rooted ones, are *not* true. If we can clear away this venerable rubbish of the past and the bigotries of the present, we shall be able to discover, I believe, an underlying core of truth that would find wide support and on which each man could build his own particular philosophy. Rational beings ought to be able to accomplish this much, and step by step to come closer to a concept of the truth on which they could unite. Our fundamental premises, at least, should be the same. Any great project, to attain its end, must be the work of men in harmony as to their basic assumptions. To make a prosperous voyage, a ship's company need to agree on where they are going, what they must do to get there and how they must work together while on board. They may have differences on some details but not on the basic facts of navigation and geography. To travel successfully on this voyage of life we should throw overboard all untenable ideas that separate us, harmonize our differences and set our course by the fixed stars of truth, so far as we can see them.

To help construct a common faith should be the concern of many thoughtful people. It is not a task for a handful of individuals, and should no more be left to theologians and philosophers than national policy should be left to politicians. The means by which this formidable task is to be undertaken cannot be considered here. It will require the exercise of constructive imagination and a vast deal of thought and labor. Perhaps this is something for UNESCO or some other international agency to sponsor. A worldwide ecumenical congress might be a practical method at the start. Certainly active discussion, formal and informal, under as many auspices as possible, is an essential preliminary.

These practical problems, however, are not our first concern. They are for activists and propagandists to attack. One necessary step must first be taken—the formulation of a general platform of belief that will appeal to men of every faith, or of no faith at all, as the basis for an approach toward philosophical and religious unity. This is a task for thoughtful men and scholars. We bear a grave responsibility to make at least a start toward such a formulation, a positive statement that will serve as a theme for discussion and a program for accomplishment. Most attempts to do this in the past have been made on behalf of some particular religion, but a program that will attract general acceptance must bring together what is best in *all* the great philosophies of the world. Speed is of the essence, for the course of history accelerates, and time, with which we once could be so lavish, is now in short supply. This is a source of danger but a source of opportunity as well. Today men think in years, not centuries, and programs that once would have taken lifetimes to complete are now accomplished almost overnight, as was shown before our startled eyes in the liberation of the states of Africa. Under the surface there are rumblings of many other changes. In such an awakened world, where religious freedom and the ecumenical spirit rapidly advance, active concern about a common faith and an intelligent discussion of the problems it presents are much more likely to take place than in the slow-paced years of Queen Victoria's time.

But why, one may ask, is it necessary today to draw up any statement for general acceptance? Are not these problems being actively discussed from thousands of platforms and pulpits and in the pages of an endless stream of publications? It is rare that any list of the ten best sellers fails to contain at least one book in the general field of religious philosophy. People are eager to read about such matters. May we not expect that, in the course of time and without undue urgency, opinion will slowly crystallize and, by a sort of natural selection of ideas, will gradually move closer to a general agreement on the major issues? This indeed may happen, and let us hope it will; but there is little evidence yet of growing unity of opinion. Churches are showing greater respect for one another's points of view and practices but there has been little actual convergence of belief. To construct a platform for a common faith on which it might be possible for *all* men to stand, since it would bring together elements from a wide range of beliefs, has rarely been attempted, presumably because it seems inherently impossible. And yet it is just this which must be brought to pass unless we admit that agreement, in the very nature of things, is quite impossible. Before we make such a concession to chaos, a vigorous attempt, I believe, should be undertaken to find a basis of agreement, at least on principles and premises.

To do this it is necessary to clarify our ideas about some of the deep problems that are involved in such a common platform: the nature of man—his mind, his soul, his spirit; the origin of his values, the existence of God, and what relations there may be between God and man. Much of the present book is given over to a discussion of these questions, but from the viewpoint of biology rather than of philosophy or theology. My own competence for such a task is inconsiderable. Philosophers will point out errors that are doubtless present in the metaphysics of an amateur; and biologists will wonder how the author happened to stray so far from the orthodoxies of his profession. Readers will miss in these pages the names of some of the great philosophers who are usually mentioned in treatments of this subject, as well as many of the theories that long have gathered around them and to which more respect, perhaps, should have been shown. These omissions come partly from my lack of professional competence but even more from a desire to direct the discussion in such a way that it is not encumbered by terminology and concepts that a layman, to whom the book primarily is directed, might find it difficult to follow.

One who undertakes to frame even a preliminary statement here will be beset on every side. Upholders of a hundred different creeds will disagree with him on almost everything except the inevitability of disagreement. The program on which I am suggesting that we unite includes ideas so radical that many, both theologians and scientists, will dissent from it. What is proposed here may prove entirely impracticable to achieve. The task is one to dismay a stout heart. It will bring bitterness of difference and—what is harder to bear—the sincere regret of many friends that I should have wandered afield so far, so fruitlessly, and in such a hopeless cause. I am supported, however, by the conviction that unless *some* general agreement can be reached, some unity achieved, our race is destined to remain so dangerously divided that its future is an uncertain one indeed. For this reason, at the risk of complete failure but in the hope of making a beginning at a task that someone else must carry further, I shall endeavor to construct in these pages a preliminary outline of what I believe are elements essential in the foundation for a common faith of men.

An encouraging fact today is that many of the minor distinctions among our beliefs are gradually beginning to disappear and that under every sky men can be sorted into two great groups: those whose faith is in the mysterious intangibles of the spirit, and those who see nothing in the universe beyond the ponderable and measurable certainties of matter and the inflexibility of natural law. These philosophies are usually termed religion and materialism. Running through all faiths of men there is this single issue, of such paramount importance that if it could be resolved all other differences would take a secondary place and could be reconciled without serious difficulty. Here is the deepest philosophical problem that man faces.

Terminology in this area is not exact. *Materialism* is related to the kindred philosophies of determinism and mechanism, and all three are usually opposed to indeterminism, finalism and vitalism, though the exact limits of each are not sharp. The first group stresses matter and natural law as the basic realities, and regard living things essentially as mechanisms. I shall use the term materialism for all three. The other group sees natural law as much less rigid, and regards life as unique and perhaps as radically different from lifelessness. Religious philosophy goes further and maintains that there is immanent in the universe a spiritual reality it calls God. The more liberal materialists accept the truth of freedom and moral responsibility, but reject completely any supernatural or divine element. Instead of materialism the word *naturalism* is often used today, as opposed to the supernatural. *Naturalist,* however, has such a familiar connotation in biology that its use in other fields is very awkward. *Religious* is not a happy word, either, since in the minds of many it carries the burden of antagonism frequently felt against organized religion. The alternatives, however, are less satisfactory. *Nonmaterialistic* is merely negative. *Tender-minded* does not go far enough. *Spiritual* for many has unfortunate overtones, and *theistic* is too narrow. Even though physics has shown that matter consists essentially of energy and thus, in a sense, has lost its ancient character, let us not forget that it is still solidly material and that there is a very practical difference between material and immaterial things.

A naturalistic philosophy still deserves the name of materialism.

To recognize that most life philosophies can be grouped into these major opposites which emerge from the welter of the faiths of men, and that the really basic question is the one posed by the difference between them, simplifies somewhat, though it makes no easier, the task of him who would attempt to draw the outline of a philosophy on which some general agreement might be reached. The clash between these giants echoes through the world. On one side stand the Communist societies as well as hosts of people in the Western world and elsewhere who look to matter and natural law as the ultimate realities; and on the other are arrayed the supporters of religious faiths, whether organized or not. This opposition is reflected to some degree even in education, where the debate between the "two cultures" of the humanities and the sciences is now so active. If the luxurious growths of mankind's minor faiths are once removed, these two great peaks that dominate the landscape can be seen more easily. To many, this clearing of the ground will remove such precious things that even to suggest it seems preposterous. One should remember, however, that many of these lesser philosophical ideas are what William James called "over-beliefs," faiths that cannot be proved true and are not essential for religion but which for some enrich its content and its usefulness. If agreement on the basic beliefs of men is to be achieved it is these two major philosophies, now apparently so far apart, that must be brought together. Many will object that this is quite impossible, since it involves the reconciliation of opposites; but in a day when many seemingly impossible ideas have been accepted, let us not be discouraged before we have made at least a trial at this one.

Materialism is no new philosophy. It has existed since the time of Democritus, but its most powerful stimulus came from the discoveries of science. These have seriously challenged many religious beliefs. As the dominant faith in that part of the world that saw the birth of modern science, Christianity has been the particular object of this challenge. Gone now are the comfortable days when so many gave it homage. A slow erosion of its basic assumptions, and those of other faiths, has long been taking place. Spirit, faith, God, mysticism of every kind—these are words from which, in many minds, the significance has gradually been drained away. Nature, say such folk, is the abode of law, not of divine caprice. In the universe known to science, where only matter and energy are the ultimate realities and everything that happens seems rigidly determined, what need is there, or even possibility, for the interposition of any God in man's affairs? In such an atmosphere materialism has thriven. Man has been its major victim. He long prided himself on his miraculous origin, but the profound conception of organic evolution has shown that the Biblical account of his beginning, save in a figurative sense, is palpably untrue. Biologists and anthropologists possess a wealth of evidence that he arose from lower forms of life over a long period of time. In his creation, they say, was no miraculous touch of the divine finger, portrayed by Michelangelo, but the normal operation of cosmic forces, impersonal, purposeless and leading nowhere.

Still more damaging to the early ideas about man's nature, though less dramatic, have been other discoveries in biology. Life, it says, is not the result of any mysterious "vital force," as used to be believed, but rather a particularly complex and well-regulated series of chemical and physical processes. The traits of organisms are determined by precise molecular configurations locked in the chromosomes of their cells. Man is biologically no different from the humblest of living creatures. As to his mind, the supreme distinction that sets him above the other animals, many psychologists find no place for such a thing at all, and regard "mental" phenomena simply as instances of complex behavior, the results of electrical processes in that amazing mechanism, the human brain. Psychology is based squarely upon physiology, and by the great majority of its practitioners any belief in a "soul" or a "spirit" in man is looked on as the curious persistence of an ancient superstition, long outgrown among intelligent folk. Materialism thus appeals to science to support a conception of man as an extraordinarily complex physicochemical mechanism, made of proteins, nucleic acids, water, minerals and many other substances. It believes he is no part of any cosmic plan, that he has no spiritual relationship to the rest of the universe, that any hope of immortality for him is preposterous, and that his high ideals and aspirations, and equally his cruelty, lust and greed, are no more than evanescent molecular ripples sweeping across the substance of his brain.

Before we begin the task of trying to bring together these two major contenders for the allegiance of mankind, it will be useful to look more closely at their strengths and weaknesses, and at the reasons for the appeal that each now makes.

Religion in the ordinary sense, materialism contends, is quite unnecessary for man's life. The Judaeo-Christian tradition, to be sure, has for centuries been the bulwark of our western morality, but unbelievers are confident that without reliance on its ethic or on any other spiritual foundation for life, a social order can be developed that will be meaningful and satisfying. But, we ask, will not a collapse of the scaffolding that so long sustained Christendom plunge into despair those men who have reluctantly become convinced of the truth of a very different way of looking at the world? In fact, this seems but rarely to occur. A few men have, indeed, been crushed, but others, taking courage, have built from the wreckage of the old faith the framework of a new one. Although appeal no longer can be made by them to God, *Man* has taken his place. In *Man* is born the high intelligence that gives him dominion over the world and even opens to his conquest the vast space outside. In *Man* arose those high ideals of unselfishness, justice, peace and altruism which, though often unattained as yet, are recognized as goals to which humanity aspires. It is *Man* who is drawn toward the magic of beauty and seeks to create it in poetry and the arts. It is *Man* whose imagination is set afire by the sublime universe in which he lives and whose emotions are often deeply stirred by experiences that used to be associated with religion. It is *Man* who feels keen sympathy for his brother men and seeks in many ways to help them. Most of the attributes so long attached to God seem in reality to belong to *Man!* He is indeed the capstone of creation.

"Glory to Man in the highest!" sings Swinburne, "for Man is the master of things."

The proponents of this scientific humanism take good heart as they look about them, and see in their new faith the promise of a brighter day. Man's future, they point out, is in his own hands now and he need not be hindered by any of the superfluous theological trappings of an earlier time. This new religion is one that faces the future, not the past. In it, they believe, lies the best hope for all the race of men. The achievements of such a naturalistic faith already are considerable. Many who enthusiastically accept it show by their lives a true devotion to human welfare. We all know men and women who profess no religion but who are blameless and full of good works. Abou ben Adhem speaks for all of them. Indeed, in the thought of the brotherhood and mutual dependence of men, free from any control outside themselves, there is something that tends to knit them hopefully and helpfully together, as if they were at sea in an open boat, embarked on a course they know not whither—save that it leads inevitably to oblivion.

In the face of this pragmatic proof that materialism is a philosophy by which many are able to live with satisfaction and success, and in the face of the support for it that science gives, how can anyone still maintain a belief in the life of the spirit, the existence of God and the other aspects of what is commonly understood as a religious faith? To reach the philosophical agreement that we seek, is not the simplest way merely to give up religion and its spiritual beliefs completely? Many will enthusiastically assent, and forecast the inevitable end of all religious life as we now know it—certainly all organized and formalized religion. This is the attitude of many intelligent folk today. We must frankly face the possibility that they are right, and that the humanist position, which denies God's existence, leaves out other concepts of theistic religion and exalts man as the highest being in the universe, is the philosophy to which we ultimately must come.

But the issue is not as simple as it seems to the materialist. Although some religionists are hypocritical and others so limited in vision that their opinions are of little value, it must nevertheless be admitted by the most stubborn materialist that there *are* hosts of men and women, and among them many of the most thoughtful and intelligent of our time, who sincerely believe the basic tenets of some religion and whose lives are profoundly influenced by such beliefs. The sincere convictions of these men of faith are difficult for materialists to understand. It seems so obvious to them that materialism is the *only* basis for a respectable philosophy that there is no room for argument on the other side. Their reaction to religionists is one of scant sympathy or respect, and often of ridicule and thinly veiled contempt. Nevertheless, the existence of widespread and intellectually defensible religious faith today, however one explains it, simply *cannot* be denied. Religion of some sort, if only a deep reverence for the illimitable and mysterious universe, is such an intrinsic part of human nature that a life philosophy which disregards it can never, I think, gain universal acceptance among the sons of men.

There are three reasons for this persistence of religion in a secular age. First, humanistic materialism is far from the universally satisfying philosophy that some would have us think it. Beneath the cheerful glow of the brotherhood of man and the enthusiasm for bringing intelligence, freedom and dignity to all humanity, lurks the heart-stopping chill of ultimate tragedy. Humanism has no answer to the problem of evil—the undeserved suffering of innocence, the frequent irrationality of life, and its final blotting out by death. Courage it may possess, and wisdom, and unselfishness, but where can it find *hope?* In thinking of these things the most convinced materialist must often hear, like the voices of the chorus in a Greek tragedy, the familiar words of Bertrand Russell:

That man is the product of causes which had no prevision of the end they were achieving; that his origin, his growth, his hopes and fears, his loves and beliefs, are but the outcome of accidental collocations of atoms; that no fire, no heroism, no intensity of thought and feeling can preserve an individual life beyond the grave; that all the labors of the ages, all the devotion, all the inspiration, all the noonday brightness of human genius, are destined to extinction in the vast death of the solar system, and that the whole temple of Man's achievement must inevitably be buried beneath the debris of a universe in ruins—all these things, if not quite beyond dispute, are yet so nearly certain that no philosophy which rejects them can hope to stand. Only within the scaffolding of these truths, only on the firm foundation of unyielding despair, can the soul's habitation henceforth be safely built.[1]

---

[1] *A Free Man's Worship,* 1918.

This somber aspect of the materialist's philosophy cannot be forgotten or ignored. It shows itself in many ways.
We live in an age of pessimism, the natural consequence of
two great wars that shook the foundations of the world.
This is conspicuous in the philosophy of existentialism and
in Protestant fundamentalism, especially in Germany.
Man's life cannot help being tragic, many tell us, for this
is the price that he must pay for having eaten of the tree of
knowledge, for having become a rational creature. Let us
face the inevitable, they say, with our eyes open and not
blurred with the fog of superstition. But is it conceivable,
asks the man of religious faith, that altruism and the sincere and unselfish love of man for man, on which the Good
Society must finally depend, can permanently be established unless it has a basis on something deeper than a
hopeless and man-centered creed?

Another reason why a naturalistic philosophy does not
sweep everything before it now is that the scientific foundation on which for so long it seemed to be established has
been seriously disturbed (See Chapter 2). Matter itself
is by no means the solid certainty it once seemed but something much less tangible and dependable. Natural law, the
august presence of which was thought to dominate the
universe, turns out to be a statement of the *odds;* long
odds, to be sure, but a very different thing from certainty.
Even reality itself may be only an aspect of probability.
Furthermore, the treasured objectivity of science, its strictly
neutral and unprejudiced observation and recording of the
facts, is not only difficult but in some cases may actually
be impossible. Earlier ideas of space and time have been
called in question. Axioms, self-evident truths, often are

not able now to vindicate their claim. Biology, seemingly at the point where it might possibly be "reduced" to a phenomenon of physics and chemistry, presents an embarrassingly difficult central problem that so far has defied solution, the problem of the *organism*. Throughout the sciences, common sense, the badge of hardheaded practicality, once thought of so highly, is now of little final use. Where space is curved and length depends on speed and matter can be changed to energy, much science of the nineteenth century seems naïve indeed. Theoretical physics still is far from a final solution for its problems, but there is a general willingness in science to draw conclusions that not long ago would have been looked upon as quite impossible. The subtleties of these new concepts are by no means widely understood, but enough has been grasped by intelligent laymen to convince them that the scientific certainties once so dogmatically asserted are certainties no longer, and that our conception of the universe, both lifeless and living, is of something much less rigid than it once was thought to be, and thus of a place more congenial to the existence of intangible things like spirit.

Much more important than either of these reasons in explaining the persistence of a fundamentally religious philosophy in the face of what may seem an overwhelming challenge to its truth is the basic difference in the foundations on which materialism and religion rest. Materialism, like science, is based on intellect, on a rational interpretation of the hard facts of nature. Its data are ultimately resolvable into logic and mathematics. A human being, and particularly his brain, seems much like a computer in principle and in method of action, and this fact is often cited as proving his essentially mechanical character. It is as a *mechanism,* many believe, that man's nature must ultimately be understood.

But a computer differs from a living person in one very important respect—it has no feelings, no emotions, no desires. At least we have every reason to believe that this is so. Strictly speaking, we cannot be sure of the existence of such qualities save in ourselves. If we should succeed in constructing a mechanism which could make clear to us that it felt pain, or liked to listen to music, or could see the point of a joke, we would be willing to concede that it experienced emotions. Such an eventuality is beyond the bounds of present possibility. A complex computer is a device that displays something very close to the *rational* behavior of a man, but it lacks the sentient, subjective qualities that he enjoys.

The significance of all this is that their emotions and sensibilities are the means by which most individuals are drawn toward a spiritual interpretation of the world. Religion is close to aesthetics. Beauty is something that we *feel,* often without understandable reason. A sunset, a work of art, a few lines of poetry or bars of music speak intimately and movingly to us. We experience their authority. They are not illusion but reality. The deepest religious experiences much resemble these. Many men *feel* that beyond themselves there is something with which they can communicate; something real, transcendent and benevolent. Such inner evidence for the truth of religious faith is far more convincing to most people than rational or scientific "proofs." Though science may seem to contradict its conclusions, religion stoutly maintains that it does touch a reality unreachable in any other way. The vivid experience, the unreasoned assurance, is for it the fundamental fact. These intuitive convictions often possess an inner authority that reason itself, however logic-tight, does not bestow. Science is man's attempt to gain an intellectual understanding of the material universe, and is being pursued with very great success today. Religion, however, seeks to understand those qualities that are immaterial. These also are of much significance for human life. There is a *practical* argument, too, in favor of religious belief: it is justified by its *fruits*. Throughout history countless men and women have found that belief in a spiritual order in the universe not only ministers to their peace of mind and makes their lives more satisfying but helps them bring to pass things that otherwise they could never have accomplished. Belief that in a sense they were partners with God has strengthened hearts and hands.

Religion, particularly organized religion, is often under attack today, but it is not without defenders. Its roots are both in superstition and in aspiration. It has been infected with almost every kind of human frailty, and many of its pages are bloody ones indeed, but through the centuries, slowly refined in faith and practice, it has borne witness to ideals of righteousness and human brotherhood. Often maintaining in a scientific age preposterous beliefs of bygone days, it strives for higher truth than any open to intellect alone. One of man's chief concerns today is to understand the meaning of religious faith and to discover what place in human life it ought to hold.

These two philosophies—the religious and the materialistic—thus differ in the very foundations upon which they rest. One's attitude toward them depends essentially on where one looks for truth. The materialist finds this in matter, energy and demonstrable fact. He scoffs at anyone who seeks it in fleeting emotions, wishful thinking and mysterious products of the imagination. To him these evidences are so obviously unreliable and deceptive that he cannot see how sane men give them credence. The man of faith replies by showing that abiding realities exist quite independently of the material base on which they rest. Which is more real, he asks, in a great painting: its canvas and its pigments or the thing of beauty which their arrangement by the artist's hand has created? Is a poem simply marks of ink on paper or is there something more involved, something that stirs the heart? The fact that religion still survives as a respectable philosophy means that for many people the most real and significant part of a man is *not* his material self or his rational faculties but his sensitivity to things that are not physical or mechanical—his love of beauty, his aspirations for goodness and truth, the promptings of his spirit. "Religion," says W. T. Stace, "is the hunger of the soul for the impossible, the unattainable, the inconceivable. . . . This impulse lies deep down in every human heart. It is of the essence of man, quite as much as is his reason."[2]

As the years pass, minor beliefs grow less significant and these two protagonists emerge as the chief contenders for the faith of men. The issue between them must be settled if any basis for agreement is finally to be reached. In recent years man's knowledge of the physical universe

---

[2] *Time and Eternity,* 1952, p. 4.

and of the nature of life and of himself has enormously increased and is proceeding at an accelerating tempo. Historians in the future will regard this "explosion" of scientific knowledge as the most important and dramatic event of our time. And yet, despite this, there is less agreement now about some of the fundamental problems that man faces than there was a hundred years ago. Instead of clearing up the debatable questions, scientific progress has often deepened ancient differences. The two protagonists still face each other grimly, and no life philosophy that resolves the differences between them has yet gained wide acceptance.

If this is a *universe* we live in, however, not a multiverse, and if such a thing as truth exists and can be reached by human effort, it should be possible to clear away much of this present conflict of opinion and to gain a larger measure of accord than now exists. Though agreement is far off, the issue is sharper than it used to be, for many of its details are now seen to be irrelevant and the two major alternatives are more clear. This suggests the hopeful possibility that the difference between them is not between black and white, between truth and falsity, but that the two may be different aspects of some fundamental reality, two different ways of looking at the universe, two highways to the truth. There are other cases, such as that of the contradiction between classical and quantum mechanics, which can be interpreted in this way, and Bohr has called such a concept *complementarity*. In this confrontation between the faiths of spirit and of matter there are many intelligent people in each camp, and one who looks at the question as objectively and impartially as possible can hardly fail to conclude that there must be *something* on each side that is worth serious consideration. This should make dogmatism pause. It suggests that truth is not with either protagonist alone, and encourages the hope that a satisfying agreement may someday be possible. We must realize, however, that an attempt to bring these two philosophies together may prove no more than wishful thinking and will finally turn out to be impossible, for rooted in the very nature of things may be an incompatible difference between the two so deep that no amount of verbal ingenuity can ever heal it.

To reach any measure of agreement will involve, for many people, a truly "agonizing reappraisal" of what they now accept as true. The first thing that must be cast aside, I believe, is dogmatic certainty. The full truth about man and the universe has not yet been reached, and confident but unsupported assertions on either side will command no universal acceptance. Many religious ideas will certainly be called into question. We cannot expect that a materialist, accepting the facts and concepts of the sciences, will agree that all Bible stories are true, that the cow is a sacred animal, that saving grace is to be gained by a pilgrimage to Mecca, or that any human being is infallible in matters of faith and morals. Let us not underestimate, however, the heartache that will often follow renunciation of an article of faith that has been accepted over many years. To do so requires a high degree of resolution. A man who gives up a cherished belief to follow one he is now convinced is truer deserves our admiration.

The materialist, on his part, must lay aside his conviction, long held and frequently expressed, that such words as "spirit," "soul" and "God" are meaningless, since they refer to things that have no real existence. To give up this conviction requires a wrench more serious than that experienced by the man of faith, for it involves changes in no single tenet of belief but in his whole attitude toward the universe.

A fundamental revision of his philosophy by either materialist or man of faith, once he has reached the years of his maturity, is most unlikely. Those who seek to alter widely the opinions of mankind must exert their efforts chiefly upon younger folk. When education, however, is devoted to mere indoctrination in ecclesiastical dogma or in the opinions of some school of thought, its major purpose becomes frustrated. Young people certainly need guidance, but this guidance should consist in opening their minds, not closing them. Only a generation brought up to think for themselves will be able to reach a good measure of agreement as to what is true.

Religion involves many different "overbeliefs" that cannot be either proved or disproved, but to some people these have an appeal so strong that they become a portion of one's personal faith. The question arises as to how firm these minor differences may be without invalidating the basic agreement that we seek. Can a person, for example, who believes in transsubstantiation, or in the efficacy of prayer wheels, have the same basic religion as one who does not share in these beliefs? Certainly not, if these form a necessary part of his religious faith; certainly not, if he thinks that all men should subscribe to them. The unified faith we seek cannot contain elements like these so long as in their *literal* form they are thought of as essential.

But if we look upon them as we do the myths and legends of our history, they may express something vitally important. George Washington's cherry tree, Johnny Appleseed, the Angel of Hadley, John Alden and Priscilla, all set forth ideals we have about our past. It is for this we reverence them, not for their literal truth. They are *symbols* of what we really believe, and symbols, in art and history and religion, often speak to us truths too deep to be stated in cold, literal terms. In this sense, many elements in a religious faith can be accepted by men who never would be able to give assent to them as doctrines that must be accepted literally. Such elements in Christianity, for example, are the doctrines of the Apostolic Succession, the Atonement and the Fall of Man. So is it, I am sure, with many accounts in the Bible. These enrich our understanding of God and man without demanding from us a belief in their literal truth. They are the poetry of religion.

Though it should be possible to avoid some disagreement on many details of religious belief by regarding them thus as symbols, ideals or overbeliefs, the orthodox will vigorously maintain that ancient teachings of synagogue or church are far more than mere fairy tales. To put new wine into these old bottles will certainly be difficult indeed. Debate and argument are bound to be acrimonious, an unhappy fact that has so long prevented free discussion of such fundamental questions. But it is not the support of comforting illusions that we seek. The world is in too desperate a state today to be helped by anything less than truth. If we can cultivate everywhere an atmosphere in which men will seek it by every means at their command, and regardless of cherished beliefs they must abandon now, their intelligence and common human judgment, I believe, will bring them in time to a very considerable measure of agreement.

To stand on the common platform that we are seeking here to build, men must be *intelligent, open-minded* and of *good will.*

Intelligence they certainly require. Uneducated and provincial persons, however estimable their lives and comforting their message to like-minded men, will be of little service in resolving the doubts and reconciling the differences that trouble the minds of men who realize how difficult the problems are that must be faced. There is a place for childlike faith, but it will not overcome the perplexities of a sincere materialist. It is on the intellectual level that religion has lost its major battles with unbelief, and if the two protagonists are ever to reconcile their differences, the objections that science has so long offered to religious philosophy must be fairly met. Certainly a religionist who is to discuss these questions fruitfully must be familiar with the contributions made to them by science. The materialist must also be conversant with the arguments and point of view of religion. Too often he is theologically illiterate. Those on both sides should have some acquaintance with what the professional philosophers have had to say on these great matters. Only a man with trained intelligence and a well-stored mind will be of service in helping to build a platform of agreement on which all may stand.

Open-mindedness as well as intelligence is necessary. The greatest obstacle to agreement is that so many have prejudged the issues before meeting them, and that this prejudice prevents a fair consideration of the problems.

The fruit of prejudice is dogmatism. Religion has frequently, and often rightly, been accused of this, but some materialists are dogmatic, too. They are so sure of their presuppositions that it seems never to occur to them that they may be wrong.

Perhaps more important ultimately than these first two qualities is the third one mentioned, for without true friendliness and good will, any attempt at agreement will be hopeless. Difference of opinion often leads to enmity. If a person does not think as we do he is, perforce, a stranger and thus suspect. This is the worst form of xenophobia. Strength of argument is essential, but unless this is joined by a sincere desire for the welfare of those who disagree with us, it is indeed but sounding brass and a tinkling cymbal. Our opponents must believe we wish them well if we are to convince their hearts as well as their minds.

There are signs today that the sort of undertaking we have been suggesting may not be entirely hopeless. Many religious leaders are showing greater understanding of beliefs that are different from their own, and the ecumenical spirit is abroad. Men of faith have more understanding of science—the basis of materialism—than they did a generation or two ago. More important, perhaps, is the fact that opposition to religious ideas, once voiced so vigorously by many scientists, is heard less often now. This does not mean that science supports organized religion, or that many men of science are not antireligious, but rather that a scientist can be religious, in the broad sense of that word, and still maintain his intellectual integrity. The temper of science today favors a more tentative approach to its philosophical conclusions. Truth is much vaster and more complex than it once was thought to be. Many advances in the sciences have important implications for philosophy and are beginning to be explored by adventurous pioneers, but their significance for the construction of a unified life philosophy has not yet been fully examined. All this makes one more hopeful now than in the past of finding some way to bring together the materialistic and the religious points of view.

In this, it is important to understand just what we are trying to do, and what "bringing them together" really means. A materialist, at least in his more humble moments, realizes that a purely intellectual understanding of the universe gives little help in discovering some of its most important qualities, such as beauty and love. These are outside the domain of science but they are among the high values of his life. The man of religious faith, on the other hand, must employ the rational approach to the material universe that is used by the scientist, but to this he must also add what his spiritual insights tell him. He accepts the facts of science but builds around them a sound basis for his own belief.

Science, as such, has nothing to say about spiritual matters, though scientists often express a disbelief in them. Religion, as such, has nothing to say about the material universe, though men of faith naturally have opinions in such things. Both must accept the established facts as to the material world and the conclusions that can rationally be drawn from them as, for example, about the size and structure of the universe, the concept of relativity and the origin of man from lower forms of life. The important difference is in the *interpretations* that the two men put upon these facts. The materialist sees little beyond the physical data, and constructs his philosophy accordingly.

The man of faith goes much farther and interprets some of the facts of science (such as the behavior of single electrons or the phenomenon of biological organization) in ways that are in harmony with a religious belief. He carries his conclusions beyond the point where they can logically be proved, as religion always must, since much of it deals with things intellectually unprovable. He looks for the bearing of scientific facts on the concepts of religion, but he must avoid conclusions that are contrary to the results of science. If the two philosophies are to be brought together, each must endeavor to understand and respect the conclusions of the other. Exploration of the universe has hardly begun, and no one can yet be sure what methods of deciphering its secrets will be most illuminating a century from now. That the spiritual insights of religion can fruitfully be combined with the intellectual discernment and the rigorous analysis of the sciences, and that both may be accepted as safe roads to truth, is the hope of all who seek a basis for philosophical agreement among men.

This basis should be broad enough to provide for a life philosophy consistent—if this is possible—with the truths of both materialism and religion. The reader may be surprised that the present discussion of this problem centers in biology rather than in philosophy, physics, psychology or some other discipline, but it could hardly be otherwise. The *key* to the problem is the fact that man is a living organism and to be understood must be studied as such. We must try to find how his peculiarly human qualities of body, mind, soul and spirit have their basis in life itself; what the biological origin of his values may be; and, more than all, how a conception of God can be reached that will satisfy man's spiritual aspirations and also be consistent with what we know of life. One may disagree with the author's interpretation of biological facts but not, I hope, with the conclusion that biology must play a necessary part in reaching an understanding of man. Life is where matter and spirit meet. The present book undertakes the difficult task of interpreting in biological terms these various aspects of man and his relations with the universe as the necessary foundation for the common faith that we are seeking.

This foundation will resemble less that for a single building than the span holding up a great bridge, where each abutment undergirds a part of it and is connected with the rest by the framework of the bridge itself. At one end such a structure is anchored solidly in *matter*. From here a span is carried over to the abutment that is *life*. Just how life comes from matter is not yet clear, but the two are obviously very close to each other. From life, another span stretches across to the abutment representing *man*, over the familiar evolutionary highway from the higher animals to *Homo sapiens*. From man as a living organism a span stretches on to his various psychical qualities—his *mind*, his *soul*, his *spirit*; and from the last, a final one reaches across to an anchorage in what we call the *Divine*. The entire bridge, save for its original footing in matter, is concerned with one or another manifestation of life. It may well be called the Bridge of Life, which carries the philosophic traveler from the simplicities of matter into the wide territories of the spirit. Some men will pass along the bridge only a little way; others will go farther, and some will keep on to the end. To persuade them to walk side by side along it as far as they are able is a more hopeful way, I think, to progress toward human unity than by trying to force either of the two opposed philosophies to surrender to the other.

This method of approach divides the problem into separate though connected parts, each of which can be studied by itself. There will be differences as to the significance, or even the reality, of the later stages, but the division between the two protagonists will not be as deep as though it involved a single great gap. This simile of a bridge has the further advantage that it helps bring the problems of religious philosophy down from the heights of metaphysics to sharp focus on a single problem that is at the heart of all of them—the nature and potentialities of *life*. Here is the final question—not the biochemistry of protoplasm, or the molecular configuration of the genes or any other technicalities of biology, but the origin and the essential character of this strange "stirring in the dust" where matter and spirit meet. Here are the very roots of religion. Its great goal is more abundant life. Life touches something deeper than matter, more profound than science. Even if one has no reverence for the Divine, "reverence for life," in Albert Schweitzer's famous phrase, he should possess.

The task of building the bridge for which the preliminary sketch will here be drawn is one that might dismay Pontifex Maximus himself. The materials for its construction are at hand, however, and to make a start at bringing them together is the hopeful purpose of the present volume. I have come to feel so strongly the importance of this task that I am willing to risk the dissent and even the ridicule that the book will arouse, in the hope that it may make a contribution, however small, to the accomplishment of this great end.

II

THE PHYSICAL BASIS OF MATERIALISM[1]

THE NEW AND revolutionary ideas developed in the science of today have lighted the torch of man's imagination. Never since the great days of the Renaissance has he felt so vividly the immanence of high discovery and the limitless possibilities that lie before him. His environment has enormously expanded. It is no longer circumscribed by miles and days, nor limited to objects readily accessible to the senses. The universe is so incomparably vast that it must be described in terms that not even a government's budget has to use. Its age is measured in billions of years. Our acquaintance with it extends from electrons, bits of matter so tiny that it takes a billion billion billion to weigh a gram, to galaxies so far away that light from them requires billions of light years to reach the earth. Adventure once was limited to exploration on the surface of the globe, but man now pushes out his new frontiers into the very depths of space. Not only has the scale of the universe changed but our conception of its very nature. Nothing seems to startle a physicist today, and conclusions seemingly most improbable may well be true.

---

[1] The author is grateful to his friend and colleague Prof. Henry Margenau for having read this chapter in manuscript.

Excitement in the years ahead will come not only through experiment and exploration but in the realm of new ideas. Astronauts will lead lives of high adventure, but even more so will philosophers.

The problems of philosophy, and particularly the great questions we are here beginning to discuss, have been profoundly affected by these developments of science in the last two generations. Physics, especially, has found important new insights that altered many of its earlier ways of thinking. Nowadays a theoretical physicist, almost of necessity, must be a philosopher, for the very nature of his calling compels him to deal with the ultimate character of the material world. Therefore it is not strange that some of the most notable contributions to philosophy in recent years have been made by men who first approached its problems through physics—Eddington, Jeans, Pauli, Bohr, Bridgman, Schrödinger, Heisenberg, Margenau and others. Their work has answered some of the old questions but it has raised many new ones, too, and not all physicists agree as to how these should be met. Physics has not yet settled down to the comfortable agreements and assurances that it had in the late years of the nineteenth century, when all that seemed to lie ahead of it was the refinement of its computations to another decimal place or two. In our attempt to find how a materialistic and a nonmaterialistic philosophy may be reconciled, the developments of modern physics are therefore of very great significance.

The basis of materialism is in matter, and here is one of the main piers to which will be anchored the bridge between matter and spirit that I hope to build. Our senses reveal to us material objects that we can see, touch, hear,

smell and taste; objects that occupy space and are ponderable. They are reassuringly substantial. It is these things,
many tell us, that *really* exist, and whatever cannot be
designated by a substantive noun, however significant it
may be in other ways, exists only as an attribute of some
material object. A leaf is material, but its color, shape and
structural relations are adjectival. A man's body is material
but his thoughts are not. Such nonmaterial qualities, they
say, are real but only in a sense secondary to the inherent
reality of the material thing with which they are associated.

From the day when men first began to think about such
questions, the more tough-minded have looked on matter
in this way, and through the centuries many have agreed
with them. Modern science has been primarily concerned
with the laws that govern the character, movement and
behavior of material things. The physicist, the chemist and
the biologist have dealt so exclusively with these that everything else—thoughts, emotions, ideals, aesthetic values and
mental qualities generally—are looked upon by many as in
a sense secondary; as epiphenomena, depending for their
existence on a substratum of matter. From the day when
laws of science began to be formulated and men saw their
implications for philosophy, materialism received vigorous
support.

From Democritus first came the suggestion that matter
in all its forms consists of tiny particles, the *atoms,* so
named because they could not be cut up into anything
still smaller. This philosophy of atomism has been abun-
dantly supported by the discoveries of chemistry and physics, which are based on a knowledge about atoms. Each
of the elements has its distinctive atom which combines

with others in precise fashions to form molecules, the basis of specific substances. Atoms are the units of all material things—gases, liquids, and solids. We may well say, in the words of Scripture, that without them there was not anything made that was made.

Until about the end of the nineteenth century these atoms were thought to be very minute pellets of matter, something like tiny bird-shot or ball bearings. Models of them were constructed showing their relations to other atoms, and such models still are useful for many purposes. Discoveries made near the century's turn, however, especially the development of the unexpected concepts of relativity and of quantum mechanics, turned physics topsy-turvy so far as the ultimate basis of matter and energy was concerned. In the process its whole conceptual framework became altered. The old rules hold for objects in the everyday world of experience, objects large enough to see and touch, but for the atomic realm below this our ideas have been radically altered. Strange things are true here, and such unexpected concepts are needed to interpret them that the student of physics must learn to think in quite a different way from what he did two generations ago. One of the first things a young physicist must be taught as he enters the laboratory is that "common sense" will be of little use to him there.

The general character of the atom itself, because of its fateful implications for our lives, is now familiar to most people. It is not material in the traditional sense at all but consists mainly of energy. In its center is the nucleus or proton, bearing a positive charge of electricity and containing almost the entire mass of the atom. Spinning around the nucleus in precise orbits and at very high speeds are one or more electrons, each a very tiny bit of matter and bearing a negative electric charge. Associated with these are other "ultimate" particles, the neutrons, mesons, positrons and more than a score or so beside. In the hydrogen atom there is a single proton and a single electron. The atoms of the other natural elements have more electrons up to the heaviest one, uranium, with 92. There are as many positive charges in the nucleus of an atom as there are electrons in orbit around it. Most of the atom is empty space. If an entire hydrogen atom were enlarged to the size of the concourse in the Grand Central Station in New York, the nucleus would be about the size of a tiny speck of dust in the center of it, and the electron's orbit would lie just inside the walls. Of such nebulous stuff is matter made. This is far indeed from the reassuringly solid foundation on which the philosophy of materialism so long was based. Matter is hardly material any more. As Margenau puts it, "Materialism is no longer the comfortable doctrine it used to be, and we may dismiss it as having lost its major point."[2] We should remember, however, that this conclusion does not mean the end of materialistic philosophies. Matter exists and still is formidable.

Our concepts of matter have suffered other changes, too. The atom characteristic of one chemical element may be altered, by the addition or loss of electrons and of charges in the nucleus, to an atom of another element, and thus the old dream of the alchemists has now come true.

---

[2] *Open Vistas*, p. 127.

Sometimes this happens naturally, as when an atom of uranium[238], through the loss of alpha particles by radiation, is transformed to an isotope of lead, Pb^{206}. The rate of this process is known, so that the presumptive amount of Pb^{206} at the beginning of the universe can be compared to its amount today and an estimate thus made of the age of the universe. Even more radical changes may be brought about by artificial means. Matter evidently is not the eternally unchanging stuff our fathers thought it was.

Of more ominous importance to us now is the fact that the vast amount of energy held quietly in the atomic nucleus may suddenly be released by appropriate mechanisms and cause devastating changes outside. Einstein's demonstration that energy is proportional to mass and that the energy in a system equals the mass of the system multiplied by the square of the velocity of light ($E = mc^2$) show the unimaginably vast store of power now locked up in matter. Its release provides the almost limitless quantities pouring from the sun and the stars. The proof that matter can be converted to energy is one of the great discoveries of our century, with profound philosophical as well as practical implications.

Matter is really a local expression of energy, and around it there are *fields of force* which act at a distance and not through intervening matter. As Professor Kirtley Mather has put it, "Fields are universal, virtually infinite, presumably eternal; they display internal consistency and are therefore intelligible; they come as near to being ultimate causes as the mind can grasp. They cannot be directly experienced by sense perception, but their reality is now beyond challenge."[3] These immaterial agencies may have important implications for the problems we shall be discussing.

Beneath all these ideas about matter is the fact that the most useful way for a physicist to discuss it is not in terms of models but as a series of mathematical symbols and the equations which they satisfy. Beneath these symbols and equations our familiar matter has disappeared, and the solid stuff we used to know is reduced to a shadowy symbolism as immaterial as a thought or an emotion.

Other ideas that would have seemed absurd and unbelievable not many years ago are emerging from studies of astrophysics and cosmogony. One of these is the belief that the universe is expanding and that galaxies outside our own are rushing away from us with speeds that increase with their distance from us. This is inferred from the fact that in galaxies known to be farther away than others, the spectrum of the light from them is shifted toward the red end, which can be explained only by an increasing speed of recession from us. Ultimately, some believe, these galaxies presumably will pass out of our sight. Why, then, one may ask, if this has been going on for countless millennia, have not all the stars vanished and the night sky become completely dark? One answer to this question that has found support is that matter is continually being *created* and is becoming aggregated into new galaxies. There is also evidence that matter may be destroyed as well as created, for if it meets what is called antimatter, of opposite elec-

---

[3] *Geology or Genesis* ("Main Currents in Modern Thought,") Vol. XXI, pp. 10–17, 1964.

tric charge, both types will disappear! These ideas as to the creation and the destruction of matter are so completely different from the earlier assumptions of the physical sciences that they emphasize the radical changes that have come over our conceptions about the physical world. It is no wonder that old textbooks of physics were tossed out of the window as men were obliged to revise entirely their ideas about matter and energy.

Other conclusions of the physical sciences also stagger the imagination. One was established by the famous experiment of Michelson and Morley on the speed of light, as far back as 1885. In those days, and for a good while afterward, the question was being actively discussed as to how waves of light are transmitted from one place to another. Surely, it was argued, waves must be movements *in* something, as waves in the ocean result from movements in water. The substance—perhaps a form of matter—in which light waves moved was thought by many to be the *ether,* something that filled all space. If this were true, the speed of light should appear greater to an observer who moves toward its source than to one who stands still, just as the sound made by a distant object comes faster to the person who speeds toward it. Michelson and Morley, in a skillfully planned experiment, measured the speed of light as it moved in the direction parallel to the earth's movement and also as it moved at right angles to this. In the former case it should have appeared slightly faster than in the latter, if light were carried in the ether. Actually, no difference in speed in the two directions could be found. This astonishing result can only mean that whether a body is moving toward a source of light or away from it, and regardless of the speed of the moving body, the light reaching it will always be found to be traveling at the same speed, approximately 186,000 miles a second. This result was so hard to understand that the experimental results long were questioned, but they have stood up stubbornly. To explain them, Einstein in 1905 threw out the ether hypothesis entirely and proposed the theory of relativity.

This great new concept accounted for the Michelson-Morley result by assuming that the speed of light was always and everywhere constant and was the maximum speed possible. When further generalized, it also explained other facts that had been hard to account for, and led to predictions which were fulfilled, such as the apparent position of heavenly bodies with reference to the sun's disk during a total eclipse. It confirmed the idea that force need not always act through material things, as in a row of dominoes or in the transmission of heat, but can act at a distance, across space that is empty of any material content. Relativity thus gave a new interpretation to gravity and even to space itself, for Einstein showed that space must be *curved,* and that a particle following a straight path may even finally come back to where it began its course. Furthermore, if a clock travels very rapidly, its mechanism slows down as compared to one that it leaves behind, so that, paradoxically, a person moving with it through space would grow older more slowly than his earth-bound twin brother! The theory also shows that an object moving at high speed must increase in mass (weight), and also must become shorter in the direction parallel to its motion. The various aspects and implications of the theory of relativity involve highly technical matters that cannot further be discussed here. They are mentioned because of the profound effects they have had on our ideas of space, time, matter, energy and the very nature of the universe, and because of the serious blows they deal to the more naïve type of materialistic philosophy.

Another advance in the science of physics is of great importance for philosophy because of its bearing on our conceptions of atomic behavior, determinism, natural law and even reality itself. It concerns what is known as *quantum* mechanics, which in a number of respects violates the old ideas of *classical* mechanics. In classical mechanics, as in ordinary life, we think of energy as being transmitted in a continuous stream, as in the motion of a piston or the throwing of a ball or the passage of an electric current. At the macroscopic level this is true but it meets with serious difficulties when one examines energy transmission in objects of atomic size. Here one discovers a very different situation, for energy is not given off in a stream but in separate packets or *quanta,* each of which is observed as a unit. In a sense, the quantum theory thus does for energy what the atomic theory did for matter.

The basis of quantum mechanics is too complex to discuss here. The concept began with a study of the spectrum of light coming from a black body heated to various degrees of incandescence. The results of this could be interpreted only if light were being emitted in small packets or *photons* (each a quantum of light), the energy in which was proportional to a constant $h,$ now called Planck's constant. This is a radically different idea from the classical one that light moved in waves. There has been much debate as to whether, indeed, light does consist of waves or of particles. There is much evidence for its wave character, such as the interference patterns it forms when it is passed through a very small opening. Other evidence, notably from the so-called photoelectric effect, strongly favors the concept that it is a series of particles. Bohr has suggested that these are two different but complementary ways of looking at the same thing. This concept of *complementarity* has also been applied to the contrasting aspects of other phenomena than these, such as between the physico-chemical character of life and its organismic or biological one, and between the physiological changes in the brain and the introspective data of consciousness that accompany them. The idea of complementarity, like any philosophical dualism, is rather unsatisfactory, however, and various attempts have been made to resolve it, one of which will shortly be discussed as an illustration of the paradoxes that confront the student of theoretical physics today.

The similarity is at once evident between quanta (particulate units of energy) and electrons (particulate units of matter). Both are very small and both move at high speeds. On a given orbit about the atomic nucleus, an electron has a certain definite amount of energy and this is different in different orbits. When the electron "jumps" from an orbit of relatively high energy to one of lower, the energy it loses is released as a new photon. If it jumps to an orbit of higher energy, a photon is absorbed.

The paradox of particle vs. wave, most clearly seen in the photon, is present in the electron as well. This has long been regarded as a unit of matter, and thus a particle. It has mass and carries an electrical charge, qualities impossible for a wave to possess, and there is further evidence of its particulate nature. For other reasons, however, the remarkable conclusion seems necessary that the electron is a wave, for beams of electrons suffer diffraction when passed through a ruled grating, just as light does, and thus show interference patterns. They can be polarized, as light can be. It is these resemblances to light, indeed, that make the electron microscope possible.

This problem as to the nature of the electron raises a very important philosophical question. If the electron is regarded as *either* a wave or a particle, the other alternative seems to be ruled out and the cogent evidence for it must be disregarded. If it is thought of as *both* a particle and a wave, however, the conclusion also obviously meets with grave conceptual difficulties. To look on these two qualities as complementary aspects of what is essentially the same thing is unsatisfactory, despite the distinguished sponsorship of this idea, since it involves an intrinsic dualism.

To avoid these difficulties, Margenau suggests that the electron is *neither* a particle nor a wave! He describes an experiment in which a small beam of electrons is electrically accelerated out of a metal tube, then through a very small hole in a screen, and afterward impinges on another screen behind this one. On the latter screen the beam makes a typical diffraction pattern of concentric rings. The electrons cannot be waves while they are passing through the tube, for only *particles* can be accelerated electrically, but they certainly behave like waves in going through the small hole in the first screen, for they make a diffraction pattern on the screen beyond. On this screen they also seem like particles, for their impacts, their individual scintillations, can be seen. At one point in this experiment, therefore, the electron seems to be a particle and at another, a wave. In an experiment where there are *two* holes in the first screen, evidence indicates that a given electron must pass through both holes at once!

From such experiments, the results of which seem so irreconcilable, Margenau comes to the radical conclusion that an electron *does not have a definite position at every instant of time.* At some times its position can be clearly established but at others, as when it apparently is passing through *both* holes in the screen, no determinate position can be assigned to it. It may even be said not to exist at all. Certainly it must be something more abstract than has commonly been thought, something that can no longer be pictured by a visible model. Its characters are latent, not evident. The profound philosophical implications of such a conclusion are obvious. What, we may ask, *is* an electron?

To answer this question we must recognize the fact that the existence and position of an electron can be determined only *intermittently,* by the flash it produces as it gives off successive photons when it is bombarded by X rays. Between two such flashes, where and what is it? Does it actually exist? Margenau compares an electron to a firefly, that also produces intermittent flashes of light. In the darkness we cannot see the insect between flashes but we believe it exists because when there is light enough we *can* see it. Furthermore, the flashes are not at random but occur along a rather simple line as though the body that made them was following a continuous course, as indeed it is. If a series of positions is determined for a flashing electron, however, the surprising fact is discovered that they do *not* fall along a continuous line, as do the flashes from a firefly, but jump about in a very irregular fashion from one point to another. These points do not occur entirely at random, however, for they fall roughly somewhere within a circle corresponding to the electron orbit. Between flashes the electron has *no* demonstrable position and where it will appear at any given time *cannot be predicted*. What *can* be determined, however, is the *probability* that it will occur at any given point. The probability is considerably greater that it will appear near the orbital circle, though it is often found somewhat outside or inside this line. The important fact in all this is that although the behavior of a single particle cannot be predicted, the behavior of a large group of them can be; not with certainty, indeed, but with a very high degree of probability. This is in harmony with the now generally accepted idea that most natural laws are *statistical* ones. They are not inflexible, grounded in mathematical certainties, but are the sort of predictabilities on which an insurance company stakes its money or the ones with which a student of Mendelian genetics deals. The length of an individual life, or the presence in a genetic population of an individual with a particular combination of characters, cannot be predicted with certainty, but its probability can be. The larger the number of individuals, the closer will the result be to expectation and the greater the probability of a given outcome. In the relatively large bodies dealt with in classical mechanics probabilities are so high that the results, for all practical purposes, are certain, and laws drawn up for them can be relied upon with safety.

Nevertheless, at the foundation of things there seems

to be no certainty. What an individual particle will do no man can tell. The very important fact emerges, however, that its course is not a purely random and aimless one, for it has a tendency, a *potentia,* as the older writers called it, to move in a given way. It is about this tendency, here and elsewhere in nature, that laws can be formulated. This is the fact that makes the world dependable, and science possible.

Some distinguished scientists do not like this idea. They believe, as Einstein did, that "God does not play dice with men." They are inclined to think that the indeterminate results of experiments follow from experimental error, from the extreme difficulty of the manipulations or from our lack at present of fundamental knowledge that would enable us to predict results with certainty.

Others, however, have become convinced that the universe is not the inflexible system we once thought it was. One evidence of this is the fact that although the course of a large beam of electrons can be predicted accurately, that of a single electron cannot. Another notable expression of this is Heisenberg's principle of uncertainty, or indeterminacy, which states that although both the location and the momentum of a particle at the quantum level can be determined, they cannot be determined *at the same time,* for when one is pinned down, the other is uncertain. The observer is somewhat like a man trying to catch two grasshoppers in one hand. When he gets one he must open his hand to catch the other and thus lets the first one go. There seems to be a core of uncertainty at the very heart of nature. Things are not caught in the jaws of a fate that is completely inexorable. There is room in the atom for decision and choice—and so perhaps in us, as well. These concepts as to natural law and determinism are obviously of the utmost significance for philosophical problems. I have been greatly impressed by them in recent years, and they have had an important part in the development of the ideas set forth in the present book.

Another conclusion drawn by most students of quantum mechanics touches the very heart of science itself. It has always been the glory of the sciences that they were strictly objective. The man of science, so far as he was true to his great tradition, was an impartial observer of the facts of nature. He met with certain difficulties, of course. Sometimes the tools he was obliged to use were imperfect and failed to give him a true report; sometimes there were other factors that prevented accurate observations, but the role of a disinterested spectator was his essential one and a vital factor in the success that he achieved. The method of experiment, so important in the development of science, is a means by which objective observations can be controlled more precisely. An understanding of quantum mechanics, however, has radically changed this relation between observer and observed. Where the objects being studied are electrons or other minute particles subject to quantum laws, the instruments for observation and measurement, themselves subject to the laws of classical mechanics, necessarily affect the results that the observer obtains as to the behavior of these very tiny objects. A wide range of possible events is open in the behavior of a particle but the very act of observation puts into the record, so to speak, *one* of these events, when the *possible* becomes the *actual*. Another observation, however, may record a very different event, even though conditions remain the same. The results obtained therefore depend in considerable measure on the act of observation itself. True objectivity is quite possible to reach in dealing with larger bodies that are subject to the laws of classical mechanics, and the observer is confident that he can act quite disinterestedly and that the results of an experiment, under constant conditions, will always be the same. Under quantum rules, however, with the best will in the world, he cannot be completely objective since he himself affects the result of the experiment by observing it. The much-prized objectivity of scientific observation is impossible to obtain at this level. At the foundation of the practice of scientific investigation, therefore, lies this difficulty inherent in the very nature of things.

Finally, there is an important metaphysical question related to these concepts of quantum mechanics, namely, the problem of *reality*. At the basis of any philosophy must be an answer to the question as to what actually exists, what is *real*. Many nonmaterial things, in one sense, are real, such as feelings, ideas and values. In the material world, however, reality seems particularly to inhere in objects that can be seen, felt or otherwise sensed. In these things, many believe, lies the basis of reality, and in this fact is the source of the philosophy of materialism. Since these larger objects, however, are composed of atoms and their constituent particles, it is essential to inquire what is real in the domain of quantum mechanics. Here individual events are unpredictable, and laws, the laws of probability, are manifest only in the behavior of large aggregates of these events. But what about the reality of a single particle? At the moment when it is observed, we must admit that it actually exists at this particular time and place. But the problem is not so simple as this. We have seen that the very act of observation marks the transition, as to the location of the particle, from possibility to actuality. At the next instant, observation may show it in quite a different position. There is no relation between these positions, no law to which we can appeal to help us predict with certainty. *Between* the photon flashes of an electron, there is no certainty that the electron actually exists, or if it does, that it is in one place and not in several at once. What we can count on, however, is the *probability* that it will next appear in one place rather than another. These probabilities are by no means equal, for they are much greater for the electron's appearance in certain places than in others. It is with regard to probabilities that laws can be discovered. In a search, therefore, for something at this basic level that is *real,* some philosophers, notably Margenau, are inclined to reject the individual, unpredictable, lawless particle or event and to invest with reality, as being constant and dependable, the system of *probabilities* manifested by an aggregate of these events.

To endow such an intangible thing as probability with a measure of reality seems a very radical conclusion, but it can be defended. If the universe consists essentially of a vast system of probabilities with regard to the behavior of its ultimate particles, rather than a system the behavior of which is inexorably determined, the foundation is provided for a philosophy, although a very different one from most of those proposed in the past. It seems to me that the primary significance of these developments in physics is not for physics alone but for the sciences of life and of man, which are closely involved with physics since a living organism is a physical system, formed of matter and activated by energy. It is around the problems of biology and psychology that the contrast between materialistic (naturalistic) and religious philosophies, the subjects I shall chiefly discuss here, is most conspicuous. These sciences tend still to be based on the physics of the nineteenth century rather than on the newer concepts that are now emerging. It is still too early to see what influence these will have on biology, but they are bound to be important. What we now think of as the "ultimate" problems of philosophy, the ones on which we here are seeking some agreement, will necessarily be concerned more with the living than with the lifeless portions of the universe, and it is to these biological problems that attention will be directed in the following pages.

III

FROM MATTER TO LIFE

THE PHYSICAL SCIENCES deal with the wide stage on which the drama of our lives is set. Matter, determinism, natural law, reality—these all are problems of deep import not only for scientists but for everyone, and must have a share in any philosophy we try to frame. What most engages our interest and concern, however, is not the material framework of this stage but the drama that is being played upon it, and especially the performers who enact their lives there. Here is introduced a different element altogether. Human beings are material systems, to be sure, and subject to the laws of nature, but they are *alive*. With them comes into the material world a breath of uncertainty and of excitement. They are not automata, but creatures who think and feel; whose problems center around mind, soul and spirit—the emotions, purposes, values and ideals of *men*. These problems are not concerned, save secondarily, with matter and energy but with *life*. They do not arise in atoms but in organisms. They involve the physical sciences but, in addition, they pose the fundamental problem of what life is and how it is distinct from lifelessness. Not between man and the rest of creation is the great gulf fixed, but between life and nonlife. It seems to me that life's most remarkable quality is not its physical and chemical complexity, great though this is, but the fact that it holds within itself the possibility of bringing forth, in the highest of its exemplars, those attributes that have made man but "a little lower than the angels." Life has its roots in matter but it comes to flower in the godlike attributes that man at his best displays. His ultimate problem is to find out what he really is. It is the bearing of the facts of biology on the problems of man that has concerned me more and more in recent years.

In discussing these problems, and particularly the contrast between a materialistic and a religious philosophy, we are dealing primarily with the differences between lifelessness and life. If life turns out to be a purely mechanical process and nothing more; if it can be reduced to physics and to chemistry, this will give strong support to materialism. Proof of the chemical nature of so many vital processes, of the electrical character of nervous activity and of the control of physical and mental traits by genes have often been cited as examples of such support. If from the living mechanism, however, there emerges something unlike all else in nature, on which can be based the psychical and spiritual aspects of man's life, a foundation can be laid for a different philosophy. The major problems that concern man, even those of religion itself, are therefore fundamentally problems of *biology,* as was said on an earlier page.

Before we examine these problems in detail it will be necessary to find, if we can, what life is, for on certain basic facts about it rests the whole argument that I shall here present. Life is a strange phenomenon. It began far back in the warm dawn of things as an event in the primeval ocean, and after some two billion years of slow unfolding it gave rise to man. Just how to distinguish life from lifelessness is not yet clear, and here deep questions are involved for both biology and philosophy. A living organism is the place in which the physical and the psychical, the body and what we call the mind, exist together and it is therefore where the great problems growing out of this relationship can best be studied. Let us not imagine that such questions concern ourselves alone. Wherever life is, there its issues must be faced. From the simplest creatures up to man the web of life has been continuous and unbroken, and though lowly ones lack many qualities that we possess, there is in them the germ from which all these have come.

As to our own importance in the universe, we need no persuasion, but what about those creatures that are living but not yet human? Of what significance is *life* apart from man? In the dappled sunlight under the great maple where I write there dance, in the sunny patches, swarms of tiny flies, rising and falling, milling ceaselessly about and concerned with some important step in the brief cycle of their lives. Hatched but a few hours ago, they dance and mate and lay their eggs today; and then, their cycle now complete, they die and pass from sight forever. The only significance of these ephemeral beings is to perpetuate, for one more generation, an inconsiderable species of the Diptera. Tomorrow, other swarms will hatch, and dance, and slip into oblivion. So it has been now for a million years, the thread of life continuing in countless little bodies that passed it on to offspring and returned to dust. Such beings and innumerable others have always fascinated me. Is there any significance to their petty lives? Can it be true that every sparrow's fall is noted somewhere in the great account book of the universe? And—more momentous question—is man simply a larger and longer-living creature than a midge? No answers to these questions can be given yet, but they lie at the bottom of the problems that will be considered in these pages.

In practice one can almost always distinguish a living creature from a lifeless thing, but the former has no unique quality by which it can invariably be recognized. Living things move, either rapidly, as in most animals, or more slowly, as in plants, but lifeless ones are characteristically inert. There are many machines, however, that can move, or we should have no traffic hazards. Plants and animals grow, increasing in size from egg to adult, whereas most lifeless things do not, though glaciers and mountains certainly do. Reproduction, a sort of repetitive growth, is typical of living things, but crystals show it, too, for if one is broken into pieces, each piece may grow into a perfect crystal again. Living things are characteristically sensitive to external stimulation, or are irritable, whereas most lifeless ones are not, but the "irritability" of dynamite and other unstable materials comes at once to mind. Plants and animals have very definite forms, but most lifeless things do not, though there are many exceptions to this rule.

One distinction is a general one—life is associated with a semiliquid, proteinaceous system called *protoplasm,* usually regarded as its physical basis. This is deceptively simple in appearance. Its ground material, as seen in most living cells, is usually clear and homogeneous, but it contains many very minute objects that are essential parts of it—mitochondria, microsomes, fibrils, ribosomes, membranes and larger bodies. The electron microscope has shown that each of these possesses a definite structure. In addition, there may be starch grains, oil droplets and other inclusions. How much of protoplasm, we ask, is actually *alive?* Its chief constituent, more than 95 percent in many cases, is water, which by itself clearly is lifeless. So are fat, sugar, starch and protein. There appears to be no specific living *substance* at all; but life inheres, rather, in the way these various things are related and built into a precise *system.* This is extraordinarily complex. Many chemical reactions are going on in it at the same time, and their sum makes up the metabolism of the living body. Protoplasm is the center of intense activity, but there is nothing specifically "vital" here, for the chemical and physical changes going on inside the body can take place outside it as well. They all follow physical law. The differences between "organic" and "inorganic" processes, once thought important, are quite artificial. There seems to be no sprite-like "entelechy" that steps into the activity of an organism in such a way that natural law is violated. Perhaps, as Bohr has suggested, life may be an elementary fact of the universe, like gravity, which must be accepted without our attempting to define it.

How life differs from lifelessness has long been debated. Some biologists think that the term "protoplasm" is meaningless, since life, as something different from chemical and physical processes, does not exist. Any suggestion to the contrary is "vitalism," and thus has no scientific standing. We should remember, however, that in many natural processes there are critical points where the results of the process radically change; as when, at the reduction of temperature to 0° C., liquid water suddenly becomes solid ice. Perhaps when matter reaches a certain stage of specificity and complexity, a radical change arises within it and the phenomena that we call "life" appear. Here is no place for dogmatic assertion or denial. Both biologically and philosophically, life is still very far from being understood. It is a phenomenon so subtle that perhaps it can be fully known only through *experience* of it. The biologist, studying it objectively from the outside, may not come to understand it as well as does the poet, who can *feel* what it is like.

In protoplasm comes to focus sharply the significance of materialism as a philosophy. If whatever I am is closely dependent on the protoplasm of my cells, especially those of my brain, and if all the changes that go on in protoplasm are no different from the ones that occur in lifeless nature, then life is simply a chemical process and I am a chemical machine. It is very difficult to see how freedom and responsibility can be attributes of such a mechanism, or how man's ideals and aspirations can arise in it. On the other hand, it is hard to understand how the universality of natural law can be violated in a living thing. Here is an important point where materialistic and religious philosophies lock horns, and no verbal gymnastics, however skillful, seem able to solve the difficulty. The relation between life and law is still not clearly understood, but whatever the relation is, this strange pattern that matter makes when it enters a living system involves the issues I am here discussing. Religion is rooted in *life,* and our attitude toward religion will finally depend on what we think life is.

In helping to determine the exact nature of protoplasm and how its activities are controlled, a notable recent collaboration between genetics and biochemistry is of particular importance. We have long known that genes are located in chromosomes and in a precise order there. Brilliant biochemical studies have now demonstrated the actual molecular configuration of the genes, and are the greatest advance in biology this century has seen. The story is too long to present here, but the gist of it is that a gene is made of deoxyribonucleic acid (DNA), contains an enormous number of atoms, and consists of two long strands of phosphate and sugar, tightly coiled around each other like a spiral ladder. The rungs of the ladder are formed of four specific substances, always in pairs. These pairs may be in any sequence and any number of repetitions, so that the possible combinations along the ladder are almost limitless, as would be the combinations and repetitions of four letters. The series of pairs are not indefinitely long but are interrupted occasionally by a bit of some other substance that will act, so to speak, as a period does to a sentence, marking the end of a given gene. These molecular patterns seem to be related to the synthesis of particular amino acids, the building blocks of proteins, and form "codes," some of which already have been "broken." The genes perpetuate themselves by exact division, but genes are also capable of occasional changes or mutations. The discovery that in the very molecules of which the genes are made there are inscribed, like letters ordered into words, the exact specifications for the organism that is to be produced shows how closely this is anchored to the chemical basis of its living stuff. What more proof could one require, asks a materialist, that a living thing is its molecules and nothing more?

But there *is* something more, a problem that goes deeper than the genes. In them, to be sure, the traits of an animal or plant are filed, as in a catalog or an index; but an index is not a book. You cannot read it. Genes are somewhat like the punched cards put into a computer when it is programmed. They are not the answer but they direct the organized system of the computer so that an answer is forthcoming. How genes control development is quite unknown. There are thousands of them, each determining some change or process. These must all be so controlled and interrelated in their action that they do not interfere with each other but produce a unified whole. A living thing is not a collection of parts and traits but an *organized system,* well called an *organism.* In this no part or process is an independent event but each is related to the others. All vital activities, in development, physiology and behavior, are so well regulated that a unified condition tends to be reached and then to be maintained. Plants and animals are interrelated wholes which tend to be preserved, or to be restored if changed, and which develop under precise control. They are not aggregates but *integrates.* This process of *biological organization* is the unique feature of living things. If anything distinguishes them from purely physical mechanisms, this, I believe, is it. Life is more than a series of lifeless chemical processes. These are part of it, but it transcends them and pulls them all together. I can best define life as *the process by which matter is brought to-*

gether in organized and integrated systems capable of self-perpetuation and of change.

L. J. Henderson believes that organization is a major category in nature, standing beside matter and energy. J. S. Haldane goes further and suggests that science must ultimately interpret the world of matter and energy in terms of organism and not try, as now it usually does, to explain the organism in terms of the physical sciences. The organism, product of biological organization, has been emphasized much less than many other biological facts, probably because it is so very difficult to understand. I shall try to show that in biological organization can be found the roots not only of the physical side of man but also of his psychical traits. The main argument of the present book is based on this fact of organization, the phenomenon that makes possible the bridge of life.

Organization is well shown by what happens to a bit of food, obviously lifeless and unorganized, when it enters the body of an animal. Here, after being broken down and absorbed, it is incorporated into the living system. Every molecule of it takes a precise place in this system and establishes a relationship with the rest in such a way that the character of the system is maintained. The whole body is under *control*. When the organism dies, a radical change occurs. This control is removed, the system disintegrates, and disruptive changes proceed until the body is broken down and the matter that composed it is dispersed. While the animal is alive there is something that opposes this disintegration and pulls matter together into an organized, living whole. The same integrative character is evident in growth. As the embryo develops, growth is not irregular

but at every point and in every dimension it is so exqui-
sitely correlated with growth elsewhere that a body of precise *form* emerges. Form is the visible expression of biological organization and is evident in the almost limitless
variety of animals and plants. Form is the geometry of life.

Biological organization has two somewhat different
manifestations. It maintains the organism as an individual,
and it controls the developmental changes in this individual, from egg to adult, along a precise course and to a
precise end.

The first of these is evident in what are called *homeostatic* processes, where physiological activities are regulated. Thus body temperature is kept in delicate balance,
a constant concentration of blood sugar maintained, and
levels of many other processes controlled. If any of these
gets out of line, it is brought back and the original state
restored. Indeed, the whole process of organization, involving not only physiology but growth and development of the
unified organism, may be called a complex case of homeo-
stasis. This process, in its manifestations, has some resemblance to the feedback activities now so familiar in
certain mechanisms. The changes that occur are biochemical and biophysical ones, but what integrates all these into
a single coordinated system is far from being understood.

Regulatory processes can be observed most easily in
changes in the form and structure of an organism, especially when its normal growth and development are arti-
ficially disturbed. For example, if I cut off a bit of plant
stem that contains a bud and put the base of it in soil or
water, roots will begin to appear at the cut end, and soon
a whole plant, with root and stem in normal proportions,

will be restored. Since the days of the Greeks, this method of producing new plants like the original one has been common. The significant fact is that in each case a complete new one is formed. There are numberless other instances among plants where organs, if removed, are later restored. Examples of such *regeneration* are common in many animals, also, especially in very simple forms, or in the early stages of more complex ones. The severed head-end of an angleworm forms a new tail. Claws of crabs grow out again, as do many insect organs and the snipped-off legs of tadpoles. Missing internal structures also regenerate.

A memorable instance of the restoration of a complete whole, but involving a more thorough reorganization of the individual, was studied many years ago by a German zoologist, Hans Driesch. When the fertilized egg of a sea urchin had divided once, to form a two-celled embryo, he was able by a delicate technique to separate these cells. Each now proceded to divide and grow. The dominant theory in the embryology of those days was that in the egg are a host of different "determiners" which are parceled out to the daughter cells at each successive division, thus distributing these determiners throughout the cells of the body and controlling its development until maturity is reached. On this conception, each of the two embryonic cells should have grown into *half* of a young sea urchin. Surprisingly enough, however, each of them produced a *whole* one. The fate awaiting these two cells was therefore completely changed merely by separating them. Many cases now are known of such *equifinality,* as Driesch called it, where the same developmental end product is reached over different paths.

Such simple experiments quite disproved the old theory and presented a problem to experimental embryologists that has not yet been satisfactorily solved. This work impressed me profoundly as a young biologist, and it still does.

Many similar examples are now known. In man, identical twins are produced by the separation of the first two cells of the embryo and their subsequent development into two complete individuals. In a few plants and animals, such cases of *polyembryony* occur in normal development. In many organisms, too, cells that are nearly or quite fully developed may, under particular circumstances, become embryonic again and each grow into a new individual.

The frequency with which wholes are produced from parts, naturally or as the result of experiment, shows how deeply seated in living stuff is the ability to produce a *whole individual.* If the cells remain in contact with one another, however, this tendency toward the independent development of each is replaced by the cooperation of all the cells in the formation of a larger and more inclusive whole. The individual cell, in a sense, surrenders its own wide possibilities to the production of an entire organism. What will happen to a cell no longer depends upon itself alone but upon its position in this larger system. Organization thus maintains the individuality of a living thing but in a dynamic, not a static, equilibrium. Its material content is continually changing, as can be shown by following "tagged" isotopes that enter and leave it. We are reminded of the saying of Heraclitus: "Man is like a fountain; always the same form but never the same water."

The second aspect of this process of organization, and

I believe an even more remarkable one, is the progressive change that it involves. A living thing grows and *develops*. What is maintained is, indeed, its wholeness but this is not a wholeness fixed and unaltered. A plant or an animal passes through a cycle of change from egg to maturity and old age. Its character is progressively modified. Not only does it grow in size but it changes in other ways. New structures appear and there is increasing diversity in the tissues of the older ones. One of the delights of the study of embryology is to watch this orderly progression, this controlled unfolding. Various factors are involved in such a process—gene action, hormonal mechanisms, the influence of the nervous system, and many others. This is the field of the science of morphogenesis, which explores the origin of form and structure and thus what I believe are the very roots of biology. However we may analyze this controlled development into specific factors and processes, the logistics of it, so to speak, escape us. When we realize that in every organism the genes are so integrated in their action that order, not chaos, emerges and that development unfolds *to a precise end,* we come face to face with a distinctive character of the living organism. Something in the egg itself evidently foreshadows what this end will be; and not in the egg only but presumably in every cell of the body, for where cells can be isolated and made to develop further, each grows into the same sort of individual that comes from the egg. This immanence, so to speak, of the final whole in the early stages of development, or even in single cells, can well be seen in the life histories of certain unusual organisms and in the results of some dramatic experiments.

A sponge, for example, is a lowly animal with an un-complicated body consisting of only a few kinds of cells. In a small species, Professor H. V. Wilson many years ago succeeded in disintegrating the tissues completely by gently crushing a whole sponge, under water, and passing its material through the meshes of fine muslin. By this means the individual cells, still living, were completely separated from one another. They dropped down through the water to a glass slide, there forming a small heap. After a few days, Wilson observed the surprising result that these cells began to move about a little, and that in time they mobilized to form a structure much like the sponge of which they once had been a part. Similar cells in this case seemed to attract one another but beyond this fact we have no inkling as to how the structure is reconstituted.

Something much like this but occurring naturally and without experimental interference is shown by certain of the simple slime molds, organisms somewhat intermediate between plants and animals. In them the individual is a single cell, called a myxamoeba, which resembles the familiar amoeba but is much smaller. These creep over damp surfaces, seeking the bacteria which are their food and multiplying in large numbers by the simple process of the division of each into two. At a particular time—we are not sure just what determines it—these tiny cells begin to stream over the surface toward a number of centers of aggregation. Into each center are gathered from 10,000 to 50,000 cells which now form a small elongate mass about two millimeters long. In this the cells do not fuse but retain their independence and mill around one another freely. The mass soon begins to move with a kind of gliding motion until a dry spot is found. It now stops its migration and settles into a rounded mass. The cells at the bottom of this form a firm disk that is anchored to the surface. Those along the vertical axis of the mass harden and produce a solid stalk that grows at its upper end by the addition of more cells. The bulk of the cells, still free to move, clamber upward along this stalk and finally form a spherical mass at the tip. The whole structure, between one and two millimeters high, now looks like a very small, black-headed pin. Each cell in the mass rounds up, dries out and is blown away as a spore, which may germinate into a new myxamoeba. Some other slime molds are more complex and have whorls of small branches along the main axis, each with a spore mass at its tip. The form of the whole fruiting body is characteristic for each species and is produced by free cells moving up to their final positions. There must be something in each of these cells that regulates its movement and thus foreshadows the characteristic form which the fruiting body will later assume; something similar, perhaps, to what is in the isolated cells of the sponge. This creation of an organized living system from a rabble of cells is to my mind one of the most impressive facts in nature.

A remarkable case of development toward an end that is so different from the first part of the life cycle that the process is called a metamorphosis is that by which a caterpillar grows into a butterfly. The character of this change has never ceased to impress those who observe it. The butterfly's egg hatches into an active and voracious caterpillar. When this reaches its full size it stops feeding and forms around itself a firm pupa case or cocoon, within which it seems to sleep. The tissues of the body now undergo an almost complete transformation. Through the action of phagocyte cells the muscles, intestinal tract, salivary glands and skin gradually disintegrate. Other parts also disappear until almost all that is left of the caterpillar is the heart and the nervous system. Tiny embryonic centers of new growth now appear, which use the material of the caterpillar's broken-down tissues to build the organs of an animal very different in appearance, the butterfly. Just as in the egg there is something that represents the caterpillar that will hatch from it, so in the dormant pupa the butterfly must in some way be prefigured.

These cases are examples of the presence, in growing organisms, of something that represents the *end* toward which, as the result of self-regulatory growth, development will move. The basis for this is the occurrence, in the fertilized egg, of its complement of genes. The mere presence of the genes is not enough, however. If orderly development is to take place, their myriads of specific actions must be exactly coordinated. This basic formative process is the key to organic development, and about it we understand very little. Not simply the mature state is foreshadowed in the developing organism but the entire pathway by which this will be reached—the unfolding of new structures, physiological changes, differences in dimensional growth rates and other forward steps. In short, the whole future of the organism, so far as this depends on internal factors, may be said to be represented in the cells from which it develops. The adult is somehow *immanent* in the egg. I may compare this to a phonograph disk on which a specific pattern has been impressed so that it will play a complete piece of music from start to finish. The situation also resembles that of a computer that has been programmed, for the answer it is going to give is already immanent, so to speak, in the computer's mechanism.

One must assume, I think, that there is established in the egg and in the cells of the embryo something—a norm or pattern—which prefigures the mature individual and toward the attainment of which development proceeds. In conformity to this the various activities of the organism are carried out until the end is finally attained, either in normal development or in the reconstructed development of regeneration. What this norm is we do not know, but it seems to be a pattern of some sort in protoplasm— physical, chemical, bioelectrical or other. It must differ from the metabolic processes that provide the energy that runs the organism, and evidently involves factors that *direct* these processes, much as the switch directs the course of a train. This concept that the organism in its activity *conforms to a pattern set up within it* is important, I believe, for all biology. It is basic to the ideas I shall present in these pages and will be discussed later in some detail.

What, we may ask, was the origin of the phenomenon of biological organization? Were the first living things devoid of this all-important quality of life—and thus not organisms in the real sense—and has it gradually been evolved to its present state through the agency of natural selection? Most biologists, I believe, would say "yes" to both these questions. I doubt, however, if this is so. There is little evidence from a study of primitive types today that they are deficient in this organizing power. Indeed, some of the best examples of regulated development and of regeneration are found among them. To be sure, the *complexity* of organization is much lower here, and there are different *levels* of organization, but the fact of it is present. Fossil animals and plants, too, from hundreds of millions of years ago show no less evidence of organized development than do those of today.

I think that we should look for its source not in evolutionary change but in some property of matter itself, such as crystallization. One can approach this problem best through a study of form, the most obvious expression of organization. Fantastic examples of organic form are to be seen in some of the minute, single-celled organisms, such as the radiolarians among protozoa, which have an elaborate skeletal wall provided with a symmetrical array of many emergences and spines, so that the organism much resembles a delicate and very complex crystal. Such tiny organisms occur in hundreds of different species. It seems doubtful whether natural selection could have been responsible for the evolution of these remarkable forms any more than it could have been for the development of snowflakes, which also occur in hundreds of different shapes. One is tempted to regard such organic form as a sort of protein crystallization. So far as it is such, it responds to formative factors of its own, as a true crystal does. This sort of formativeness seems to be inherent in the molecular nature of matter, not something that has slowly been acquired. One may suggest that large forms and even the more complex integration evident in the process of organization itself may also be inherent in matter when matter is exposed to a particular sort of chemical and physical environment. If so, it should be interpreted not as the result of a long evolutionary process but as a manifestation of what may be called "natural" formativeness and organizing power such as occurs, to a lesser degree, in many lifeless bodies.

Whatever its origin, I believe that biological organization is the most challenging problem in the sciences of life. To produce it, thousands of genes are correlated in their action. Scores of physiological processes go on at the same time, all in perfect harmony, to produce a self-regulated, organized, integrated, coordinated whole. These are fine words, but they do no more than state the problem. Before the tremendous fact of the organism, thoughtful biologists stand in amazement. Despite all the scientific progress the last century has seen, we seem to be little closer to the solution of this final problem than we were before.

Living matter may have some surprises for us still. Let us not underestimate its capabilities. The progress of science will doubtless reveal not only new facts but new conceptions about nature. With the methods now in use I am afraid we may be missing something creative here, not accessible by analysis alone. We are like a scientist listening to an orchestra and trying to find the secret of the harmonies he hears by making an analysis of the physics of the instruments, of the sensory and motor mechanisms of the various players and of the electrical patterns in the brain of the conductor. His search will be in vain. The most complete analysis will be useless to him, for what binds together the performance of this group of men and produces great music is something underneath it all, the orchestral *score*. Something remotely comparable to this score may be the basis of the harmonious control that produces the organism. This idea is not mysticism or scientific pessimism, though it is sometimes called such. It is a recognition of the fact that form and pattern are qualities *inherent in the universe,* both lifeless and living. They must be studied by the techniques of synthesis, not by analysis alone, as science usually has done.

New ideas about nature are continually being developed, as witness the concepts of relativity and quantum mechanics, born since the turn of the century. As we look forward to the centuries ahead must we maintain that there will never be any new concepts, such as these, about *life?* We should recognize the possibility that there are more laws to be discovered; laws of pattern, synthesis and organization, perhaps, that are concerned with the way living matter is pulled together into integrated systems and creates the varied forms that life exhibits. This is the position of the *organicist,* who stresses the philosophical importance of the organism. He stands between the *mechanist,* who believes that phenomena like organization must ultimately be explained in strictly mechanical terms, and the *vitalist,* who thinks that in life there is involved something quite different from the rest of nature, some "vital force" not amenable to physical law. The mechanist is uncomfortable as he tries to imagine how the high qualities of man can ever have been produced by a piece of molecular mechanism. The vitalist is also uncomfortable at the thought that he is advocating scientific lawlessness. Only the organicist is serene. He accepts the supremacy of natural law but believes that some of the biological facts that he observes cannot be explained by known laws but are manifestations of others that have yet to be discovered.

The two manifestations of biological organization—the *maintenance* under a variety of circumstances of a single, normal individual, and the orderly *development* of this individual from egg to adult through a specific series of changes in conformity to a precise norm—provide the basis for a biological interpretation of two facts of great importance for our discussions here: the human *individual* and his *psychical processes*. Should this interpretation prove a sound one, it will make an important contribution from the life sciences to the problems we are considering. The bridge I am trying to construct is the bridge of *life*.

IV

FROM LIFE TO MAN

ONE CAN LEARN most about any phenomenon by studying the highest examples of it. Thus man tells
us more about life than does any other species; not life in
the narrow biological sense, but life as manifest at its
highest levels.

Man is a product of the long creative processes of evolution that reach back to the first living things on earth. His
ancestors have climbed the evolutionary stairway to its
climax in the species we call *Homo sapiens*. He stands
alone there now, but not far back, as time is reckoned in
geology, some of his kinsfolk were beside him—ape-men,
cave-men, dawn-men and the rest. Many fossil forms have
been discovered that stand between the men we are and
the primitive stocks that were presumably our ancestors.
Which of these were truly human no one now can say, for
humanness is difficult to define. If one of us had been on
earth that distant day—in early Pleistocene, perhaps—
when the drama of evolution among the primates was unfolding, he would have had a hard time to determine just
where in the ascending series the first truly human being

came upon the scene. Would he have been able to put a finger on one individual and mark him as a *man,* though the parents of that creature still were animals? I am sure he would not. The problem would have been no different from trying to find, in the evolution of other living things, the first plant that was truly an American elm or the first animal a taxonomist would recognize as a white-tailed deer. Species arise by imperceptible gradations, and so, presumably, did man. He is so different from the rest of the creation, however, that from pride of place he has always ascribed to himself a unique history, different from that of every other species. In all cultures there are legends about his origin. Of these, the Bible story of creation is the finest; but however splendidly symbolic it may be, it obviously cannot be accepted as literal truth.

From somewhere in the primate stock, probably not far from the ancestors of the great apes, came the first members of the genus *Homo.* They lived in the safety of the forest, as so many of the apes do now, but as time went on they were attracted by the more abundant food in the savannahs and the open plains outside. These the more adventurous individuals explored, and finally spent much time away from the shelter of the trees. This sharpened their wits, for danger was ever present in the open. It also led to their standing upright and using only their hind limbs for locomotion, thus freeing their arms for many other activities, especially the use of tools. Shelter they found in caves, and these fixed habitations favored life in families. The discovery of fire gave them protection and warmth, and made food more available by cooking. These factors doubtless hastened the evolutionary progress of this strange creature, who was in part an ape but in part something very different.

In this progress, just what was it that lifted him above the level of the beasts and made him *man?* What is uniquely *human* about him? Purely biological evidence will not tell us much. Man, to be sure, has a definite niche in the taxonomic system of the animal kingdom. He is species *sapiens* of the genus *Homo,* and has a place among the Primates, highest of the Mammals. In his bodily anatomy and his physiology he is not very different from the great apes. You can readily tell him from them now, but once this doubtless would not have been so easy. If by any chance the "abominable snowman" should turn out to be the survivor of an ape-man species, it might be hard to decide whether to put him into a school or into a zoo.

Man's behavior is more useful in distinguishing him. Articulate speech is usually thought of as uniquely human and it is certainly one of the chief means by which his progress was made possible, but many animals have a considerable variety of calls by which they communicate with one another, though these are probably not symbols of ideas, as words are in a human tongue. Emotions, so important in man's psychic life, are by no means his alone. Darwin wrote a book on their expression among animals. To make value judgments, particularly aesthetic ones, is also commonly thought of as man's prerogative, but the bower birds of Australia decorate their playing places with brightly colored objects. There are other examples of a primitive aesthetic sense in animals, as in cases of sexual selection.

But is it not the moral sense that chiefly marks man off

from lower animals? Was ever a beast troubled by a sense of what he *ought* to do? Mother love, however, is strongly developed in many of them and, especially among gregarious species, individuals often behave in ways that are harmful to themselves but helpful to the group to which they belong. Here is the germ, at least, of altruism.

But it is evidently man's preeminence in intellect that is chiefly responsible for the dominant position he holds in the world today. Here was the source of his great advantage over other animals, many of which were far stronger and swifter than he and blessed with keener senses. Beasts have little power of manipulating the environment to their advantage and hence must depend on natural gifts for success. Man can advance because he *understands*. He is able to relate particular facts to general principles, to draw conclusions, and thus to think. Such a change made possible the ascent of our species from savagery to civilization. At the material level, in his use of tools and energy and the resources of the earth, man's intelligence was most conspicuously displayed. From bits of stone now found in barrow, cave and midden to bronze-tipped spears and finally to computers and great ships in air and space, his mind has borne fruit in a technology now so fantastic that we hesitate even to guess what it will accomplish next. Still more important is man's progress in ideas. It is not the engineers and the inventors and the developers who are responsible for the heights that he has reached but the thinkers—the Darwins and the Einsteins and the Bohrs. What a piece of work is such a man! Quintessence of the dust though he may be, he certainly is the paragon of animals, noble in reason, and infinite in faculty. Hamlet's admiration for him must be ours as well.

To understand man's place and significance in nature, a knowledge of how he came to be is evidently of great importance. That he arose through evolutionary advance from lower animals to his present state was a strange idea in the early nineteenth century, but when buttressed by the mass of evidence that Darwin gathered, intelligent people finally became convinced that it was true. This was a wrench for men brought up to accept the book of Genesis quite literally. The fact that popular opinion on such a fundamental problem *did* change, albeit slowly and not yet quite completely, encourages us to hope that in the problems we are here considering a similar agreement may in time be reached.

For more than a century, the theory of natural selection (see page 120) has been examined and tested in many ways and with many organisms, and it is now accepted as the major means by which evolutionary changes in animals and plants have been produced. It is less successful, I think, in explaining fully man's advance. In *The Descent of Man,* Darwin presented an imposing mass of evidence that natural selection is the major factor in human evolution. His physical self, assuredly, was developed by the same selective processes that operated in lower forms. The most significant change here was in his brain, for in the latter period of his history, it grew markedly in size. This made it possible for him to remember, imagine and reason, with the enormous advantages over the beasts which these abilities provided. Once the brain had reached its present size, or nearly so, even in the most primitive of men, it could be used for far more complex purposes than a savage ever could imagine, just as a computer today, built for relatively simple tasks, can be used for much more complicated ones.

Man now came to a critical point in his history, one where the whole mechanism of his evolutionary progress was to be altered. Because of his increased power of communication (chiefly by speech, at first) the experience gained by one generation could be transmitted to the next by a new sort of "heredity"—education. This is quite different from biological heredity, where the inheritance of such "acquired" characteristics is impossible and the experience gained by an individual dies with him. By this new process, experience could rapidly accumulate and change thus proceed at an accelerated pace. Such *cultural* evolution was very different from the *biological* evolution of animals and plants, which depended on the accumulation of relatively rare mutations and thus progressed at a snail's pace over millions of years. The two methods are well called the *old* evolution and the *new*. The advance of civilization has been primarily a cultural rather than a biological process. Natural selection had relatively little to do with it. It was not the man who had superior natural gifts and could thus leave behind him the most offspring, but the one who had good new ideas and could teach them to his children and thus change the minds of men, who pushed the world on to new heights. By this means, in ten thousand years or so, modern civilization developed from barbarism; a period of time in which changes undergone by animals and plants in biological evolution would hardly have been perceptible. Roughly 150,000 years ago, we think, our ancestors had ascended physically to about the level of modern man. By then, biological evolution had done for them almost all it could, in providing a well-adapted body and a brain with prodigious capacities, though still largely unused. To be sure, genetic changes in mankind have continued to occur. Races of men have developed during a relatively recent period, and in this process natural selection, in minor ways, has been effective. Dark-skinned types, for example, have proved more successful than light-skinned ones in the tropics. The chief service of natural selection to man, however, was rendered long ago in providing him with the physical means of fulfilling the demands of cultural evolution. Biological evolution makes cultural evolution possible, but does not determine the direction it will take.

This change in the character of man's advance was accompanied, and indeed was made possible, by the development in him of a faculty so different from anything found in animals that it may well be regarded, I believe, as the distinctive human trait—his *imagination*. Man seems to be the only creature able to picture to himself something more than his senses tell him, something that *is not* but *might be*. When one recognizes the possibilities that confront him, when he learns to say "if," imagination is born.

In cultural evolution, imagination is the factor that produces novelties, just as mutation does in biological evolution. When imagination appeared it must have profoundly affected all man's life. Doubtless its first results were fumbling and accidental. A man playing with a heavy stick may have injured someone, and the possibility came vaguely to his mind that such a club might be used against

a wild beast or an enemy. In some such way as this, probably, the use of tools began. Man's progress in the control
of his environment was thus made possible. The spear, the
bow, the wheel and the practices of agriculture doubtless
began as acts of the creative imagination. Even to think
and reason are related to this process, since logic involves,
among other things, the power to imagine alternatives and
possibilities. Self-consciousness, too—the ability to stand
outside one's self and recognize objectively one's own existence—a quality seemingly peculiar to man, is essentially
an act of the imagination.

Alone among all living things man is a *creator,* thanks
to his imaginative powers. He is continually putting old
thoughts into new forms, getting new ideas. Much of the
creative process, psychologists believe, takes place in the
unconscious mind, but only after the way has been pre-
pared by long, hard thinking that fills it with facts and
ideas; the raw materials, so to speak, that unconscious
creativity then proceeds to fit together in new ways. An
important fact here is that these novelties have a spon-
taneous and unpredictable element about them. A scientific experiment will always give the same, predictable
result, so long as the laws governing it are known. A poet,
however, cannot sit down and write a poem to order. True
creativity transcends determinism. It is the product of
spirit, not of intellect. As a result, science emphasizes uniformity and the unbroken rule of law. In art, on the other
hand, or any creative product of the human spirit, the
exception, the individual difference, the novelty, is emphasized. There is about it a kind of wild and untamed character very different from the predictabilities of science. In

science, to be sure, novelties can be *discovered* and this process often partakes of intuition; but in art they can be *created*. It is in art that from the beginning imagination has been most active, for man's concern with beauty gave particular opportunities for his creative powers. "Beauty," said Coleridge, "is unity in variety." To find this unity in the bewildering variety of images that throng into the artist's mind is a task of extraordinary difficulty in which he must depend for help on the creativeness of his deep self. Creativeness is found among men of science as well as among artists. The formulation of a new scientific concept is as much a creative act as is putting words together to make a masterpiece. Both, I believe, are aspects of the organizing power of life. Life itself is both a creative and an aesthetic process.

Another important fact about man and his cultural evolution is that he is distinguished not so much by what he knows, or by what he can do, or because he is the only ethical animal, as because of what he *wants*. Wanting is an aspect of man's nature often neglected by philosophers, especially biological ones. They seem to feel that scientifically it is not quite respectable; that it must somehow involve teleology, a bad word in biology. But wanting cannot be disregarded. It has strong biological roots. What man wants, physically, is much like what an animal wants —food, safety, sexual satisfaction and other material ends —but a remarkable thing about him is that when he reached a certain evolutionary level, he began to be drawn toward ends *beyond* these earlier ones, goals that he now felt were more worth pursuing. He became sensitive to beauty and love. He sought goodness, mercy and truth. He admired courage and unselfishness. These became his ideals, his *values*.[1] They are spiritual qualities. Desire for them marked him off sharply from the brutes and made him man. The theory of evolution showed how close man is to the lower animals, but thoughtful Darwinians today must also be impressed by the great gap that separates him from the highest of the other mammals, not only in mental ability, great though this one is, but in something much more subtle—these contrasting value judgments of brute and human. What a brute wants is still brutish. Though man indeed is often a brute in his behavior, and the more shockingly so because of his intelligence, something sublime shines through him, something that seems to have a different origin from competitive struggles for survival. In all his history, and increasingly with the years, his eyes have been lifted up to goals far beyond what any ape would ever seek. He has created beauty in a thousand forms, and often starved to do it. He has fed the poor, healed the sick, defended the oppressed, led forlorn hopes and performed countless deeds of high self-sacrifice. He has given himself unstintingly to the pursuit of truth. Too often, it is true, he has been grossly selfish and familiar with the seven deadly sins. He has sought power and glory for

---

[1] The term "value" is used in a great variety of meanings, a useful outline of which is given in Margenau, *Ethics and Science,* pp. 129–37. One of the simplest is to recognize two kinds of values: (1) objective ones, things that are *value*able to us in promoting success and survival, such as moral values; and (2) subjective ones, things that we *value* for their own sake, such as aesthetic values. It is chiefly but not entirely to the latter class that spiritual values belong, in the sense that I use these terms.

himself, and ridden in triumph over his enemies. He still is far from being any saint. But to me the wonder is that through the centuries so many men, of every race and station, have pressed on selflessly toward some great calling, something far beyond themselves, some high urgency which they could not resist. Even when they failed to heed this call and their jungle nature gained the mastery again, a voice within them spoke, and they remembered.

When man became a seeker of these high values, he crossed a divide in his evolutionary history and in one sense became a different sort of creature. The beginning of this change probably coincided with that from biological to cultural evolution. But why should he then have acquired these new sensitivities? Why should he have changed so much merely because he could accumulate knowledge rapidly? Few students of man have called attention to the difficulty of accounting for these higher value judgments. They are put aside as mysticism, idealism or emotionalism, and most scientists do not recognize them as raising important problems about man. Gardner Murphy, to be sure, speaks of "curious and profound hungers"[2] for many things that are not meat and drink and do not satisfy cravings for obviously material things. Curious indeed they are if it is their utility alone that has produced them. I believe that man's values are the key to his nature. In dealing with them, evolutionary theory leaves the purely morphological and behavioral level and enters one that is different and relatively unexplored.

Man's deep love for beauty, for example, and his sensi-

---

[2] *Human Potentialities,* 1962, p. 213.

tivities to it in music, poetry and the arts, stretches back through the millennia to crude beginnings in primitive man. It seems to be an innate trait of our species, but I find it hard to believe that individuals who valued this subtle quality would have been more likely to succeed and to have left more offspring than would ruder men with sensibilities much less refined. Just the opposite might be expected. It was Sparta that conquered Athens, and Attila who swept a path of ruin through the civilization of his day. Time and again a culture where arts were flourishing has been destroyed by the barbarians, but so universal is man's delight in beauty that he has always brought it back into his life again.

In the development of man's moral qualities, Darwin believed, and many others after him, that natural selection has had an important part. Mother love, the basis of altruism, is so advantageous that a mammalian species lacking it would soon become extinct. Darwin doubted that children of moral parents would survive in greater numbers than those of immoral ones, but he believed that a society or tribe whose members behaved in a moral fashion would be favored by selection in competition with other tribes. The behavior of gregarious animals, where the welfare of the individual is often subordinated to that of the group, probably had its beginnings in natural selection. Many cases are known, too, in which selection has put a premium on cooperation and mutual aid. It seems probable, therefore, that at least the rudiments of some moral values in human society are very ancient and have become hereditary through selection. Nevertheless, the basis of natural selection is the welfare of the individual or the family, an almost purely selfish goal and diametrically opposed to the essential quality of moral action. It is hard to imagine how the moral codes of the great religions and the lives of good men and women through the ages could have come about through a process which puts a premium on selfishness. The discussion as to whether the great variety of behavioral traits and value judgments man shows today are the result of natural selection or not is rather pointless since most seem to have arisen during the period of his cultural evolution in which natural selection could have little effect and which has been too short for many genetic changes to become fixed in him. It therefore is unlikely that the value judgments now so characteristic of man could have been the result of a biologically selective process in the usual sense of the term.

If this is so, where can we look for their source? Most psychologists and anthropologists maintain that such value judgments are the result of the culture pattern in which an individual lives. Many of our beliefs and attitudes certainly do come from our upbringing and environment, and doubtless many of the things we want are those we have been brought up to want. Some social scientists, however, are coming to believe that, despite environmental diversities, human beings are everywhere so much alike as far as moral feelings are concerned that we can recognize certain general principles that are valid among *all* men. The same conclusions may be drawn for other value judgments. Men are men everywhere and their values transcend their cultures.

Culture itself is modified by selection but of quite a different kind of natural selection. Most of the change in it is the result of competition between many types of things, such as social organizations, codes of behavior, desirability, or standards of excellence. Here the selective agent is not the mere fact of survival but is finally man himself, who chooses the things or qualities *to which he is most strongly attracted*. Thus the automobile has "evolved" through a continuing competition for selection by the buyer's choice. We may say, too, that in the past two centuries men with increasing frequency have selected democratic over monarchical forms of government. The great "struggle for existence" today between democracy and communism is a struggle as to which will be selected by mankind. Social customs and codes of behavior have also changed as they have come into or out of favor with men. To be sure, those cultural elements that are particularly efficient are likely to persist, but not because of the survival of inborn genetic differences in the people who practice them.

The view of man, therefore, that I shall support in these discussions is that he is not the product solely of his genes or solely of his environment, as extremists on either side maintain. Both factors certainly are important in determining what he is and does, but there is a third one, less often considered, that should not be overlooked—his autonomous character as a *man*. Much of his behavior results from the fact that he belongs to a species of very definite and persistent physical and psychical qualities. His behavior is characteristic of this particular living system. From the wealth of value judgments possible in his complex organization, those that are actually *made* are the ones in harmony with his nature. A very important fact, moreover, as will be emphasized in later pages, is that these specific human value judgments, despite some deviation,

are surprisingly similar among all mankind. The lusts of
the flesh are everywhere very diverse, but man's trinity of
supreme values—beauty, goodness and truth—are manifest in all races, climes and times. This conception that
men have certain *natural* predispositions that draw them in
particular directions and toward particular values is opposed to much of what the sciences of man maintain. We
are so accustomed to think of ourselves as the result of
random changes in our physical systems, either physiological or genetic or resulting from environmental impact,
that the idea of any inner tendencies that draw us toward
specific ends seems scientifically quite unorthodox. As one
observes the similarity among all men in the things they
value, however, one cannot help being impressed with the
spiritual sensitivities men have in common. Nothing in this
idea, it seems to me, need violate biological regularity.
There are physiological and biochemical qualities that all
men share. Why should not similarities extend to the
nervous system and thus induce the pursuit of specific
values? Our values tell us something about ourselves, and
what they tell is so important that man's value-seeking is
the most significant thing about him. I believe it gives us a
clue as to his essential nature.

Even though man thus tends to make particular choices
and at his best to direct his course toward the realization
of certain high values, he has other inborn qualities, and
very ancient ones, that oppose these higher tendencies. He
is continually tempted to relax and to become no more
than an intelligent but unambitious and pleasure-loving
beast. To shake men out of such complacency and show
them how rewarding their unrealized potencies can be is

the task of all great leaders. Man's material productivity, increasing now at such a tremendous rate, will necessarily slow down for want of raw material, and his control over nature will reach a point where he will be concerned primarily not with getting a living but with using his greatly increased leisure—almost all his time, perhaps—to attaining a life more satisfying than mere physical existence. His major objective will be to cultivate, in cooperation with his fellows, the sciences, the arts, philosophy and the pursuit of truth, and to realize the almost limitless possibilities with which natural selection has endowed him, to attain the highest values that draw him. Man's objective now is not to make superior individuals reproduce themselves more efficiently but to make more individuals superior. Greatness will not be the result of evolution but of aspiration.

All this makes it important to study man from every point of view. To provide as clear an understanding as possible of what he is and what he might become is perhaps the surest way to develop the common philosophical foundation that we are seeking. When we examine him physiologically and statistically, psychoanalyze him and subject him to every test that science has devised, we still fall short of learning everything about him. There is another important source of knowledge, however, for we are *inside* a specimen of *Homo sapiens,* and from this favored place can gain a very different view of what he is, a view that introduces us directly to something quite different from his intellect—to his emotions, to his loves and hates and aspirations, his joys and sorrows, hopes and fears, anxieties and regrets; to his sensitivity to beauty and to virtue. These things, of very great importance to him, he *experiences* and thus gets the very taste of what they are. Such experiences are *his own* and shared by no one else.

Introspection is an outmoded method in psychology but it still can tell us much. It shows that a man is far more than a purely rational being. Sometimes he is such; but cool, impersonal reason, proceeding inexorably from premise to conclusion and almost machine-like in the way it operates, is much less common in us than a warmth of *feeling,* flooding through the channels of the mind and pushing, in this direction and in that, our course of action. Man is a curiously double being, partly the "natural" creature, feeling and desiring, that has climbed the branches of the evolutionary tree, and partly the rational one, born since he gained the power to think and to create. Side by side with his intellectual powers that are centered in his cerebrum is the backlog of instinctive tendencies that have come down to him from his past and seem to have their origin in the thalamus. Man has no instincts (or very few) like those of animals, preformed and ready to be released by a specific stimulus, but much of his psychic life, nevertheless, consists of urgencies and desires, though less precisely patterned. A recognition of these two aspects of his nature, so different in character and origin is necessary for an understanding of what the problems are that he presents.

Biologists often fail to recognize the complexity of living stuff, but even more do those who study man tend to underestimate *his* potentialities. Through untold generations, biological evolution had been plodding slowly forward, but with the origin of man a critical point was reached, and in a short time, geologically speaking, he surged ahead and made the world his empire. As an explorer, climbing up a mountain pass and coming to the top, sees spread before him a region vast and unexplored, so one who traces man's upward course through his animal ancestry suddenly finds in him a far more spacious prospect, stretching to the limitless future. In his tissues, and particularly in the fantastic complex of his nervous system, qualities emerge that are unknown in any other living creature: self-consciousness, imagination, a reverence for immaterial values and longings for strange things a beast can never understand. The capacities of his mind are still unplumbed, and the creative powers of his spirit no one knows. As evolutionists we follow his history out of the past, but we should also consider what the endless future may have in store for him. The wildest imagination cannot guess what it may be. Though we condemn his beastliness, we often fail to recognize that in him something new and transcendent has emerged on earth—a creature that no longer is a stranger in the universe, but from his listening post at the edge of time and space can begin to learn its secrets. Often he disappoints us by his wickedness and his use of these great gifts to gain but temporary pleasure, neglecting what would yield him far more satisfaction and what is, indeed, his bounden task—to seek and find the truth.

In a world where the pace of cultural change accelerates and may get out of hand, it is fortunate that life itself is extraordinarily conservative. In recent centuries the great alterations man has made in the way he lives and thinks, in the very basis of his culture, have swept much of the past away. They fill us with an uneasy sense of the impermanence of things. Yet, all the while, the living stuff of which we are composed is little changed from what it was thousands of years ago. The nightingales in Samarkand today sing the same song that Alexander heard. Nature guards from change by outer circumstance the precious stuff of which her types are built. Each generation has a fresh, clean start. Barring atomic accident or folly, we can count on the essential permanence of human nature into the future as far as we can see. If we fail to achieve our present ends, nothing is finally lost and we can begin over again. Our genes have not been altered. The glowing possibility of success, however, is tempered by the very real chance of failure. Civilization does not necessarily have a happy ending. Indeed, as we are likely to forget, most civilizations have collapsed in chaos or destruction. This is why thoughtful people are now anxious to rally the ranks of men and give them a unifying basis for their lives which will prevent the catastrophe that could so easily occur. Does man, this species so mercurial but so immutable, this unstable and yet unchanging creature, possess the wisdom to look clearly into nature, discuss wisely with his fellows what should be done to meet its problems, and thus assure a hopeful future for the world? Only time will tell.

In the long bridge that I am trying to construct, the abutment that stands for man is the center of the whole, and binds them all together. It closely touches matter and life, on one side, and the fruits of mind and spirit, on the other. In their interpretation of man's nature the two philosophies we have been discussing face each other here in sharpest contrast. If this portion of the bridge collapses, the rest of it no longer has a meaning.

V

FROM LIFE TO SELF

THE KEY TO THE common faith which is
the goal of these discussions will be found, I think, in the
fact of biological organization. The two distinctive products
of this process, as we have seen (Chapter 3), are *individuality* and *regulation to ends*. These are the qualities of life
least understood. What pulls together the separate parts
and processes of a plant or animal and knits them into an
organism, and what draws this organism toward a developmental goal prefigured in its living stuff—these are problems where the confident progress of biology has made
but little headway. How to attack them is not easy to determine. It is in this area, however, that one must search for
the biological basis of those problems that have a necessary
place in any religious philosophy we may try to frame—
self, personality, the soul, motives, values, morals and
ideals. I shall try to find what significance these two basic
phenomena, manifest at the lower levels of life, may have
for the highest of living creatures, man himself. If biology
can help anywhere in our present quest it will be, I think,
in what it has to say about individuality and goal-seeking

among living things. It was a recognition of these relations between biological facts and the life of man that turned my attention to the philosophical ideas presented in these pages.

Unlike so many material phenomena, life does not occur in continuous masses. The organizing process produces not only organisms but *individual* organisms, each a separate and functioning whole. Among certain lower forms, such as a reef of coral or a spreading mat of turf, it sometimes is not easy to distinguish between an individual and a group of them, united into a continuum, but even in such cases there are almost always centers of development, the beginnings of separate organisms. Among all higher forms, life exists only in these sharply distinct centers of experience and action.

The process of individuation can also be seen below the level of the organism. A cell has a life of its own. Some biologists—I am not among them—are inclined to look upon it as the true living individual and to regard a many-celled organism as a colonial group of cells. Multiple organs such as leaves in plants and metameres in animals have a semi-independent life and show a certain degree of individuality, though as parts of a larger whole.

The biological individual is not a static system like a machine. It is a center of unceasing activity. An organism is in a continual process of *becoming*. Matter is constantly entering and leaving it as new tissues are built up and old ones broken down. There is a ceaseless turnover of material, which can be followed by the use of tagged isotopes. Despite this constant change, *the individual remains itself*. In this material flux it stubbornly keeps its own specific identity. Unlike homogeneous matter, each individual has a *history* and changes showly with time. That it can maintain the delicate equilibrium necessary for life is hard enough to explain, but how through its entire existence it preserves its own distinctive character is a problem deeper still. The unity of the individual shown in bodily development is also extended, in animals, to a unity in behavior, for each individual tends to have a consistent pattern of action, an individuality in what it does as well as in how it is constructed. This is maintained by the integrating action of the nervous system.

The members of any species, individuals though they may be, show no monotonous uniformity. Among them there is much variation, and in an animal like man, compounded over the millennia from a wide mixture of racial differences, this diversity is particularly conspicuous. The individual variations result from the action of many thousands of genes, distributed in a precise order among twenty-three pairs of chromosomes in each cell. In the transfer of these genes from parent to offspring, the mechanism of Mendelian inheritance assures that there shall be a wholesale shuffling and reassortment so that almost limitless new genetic combinations are continually being produced. As a result of this, the likelihood that any human individual is genetically a duplicate of any other one on earth (identical twins excepted) or even of anyone who has ever lived, is infinitesimally small. Human beings are not turned out by a process of mass production but every individual, so to speak, is custom made to his own genetic specifications. There is no bureau of standards to preserve uniformity here. In the real sense of the word every man is unique, as his fingerprints prove. The sacredness of the distinctive human *individual,* one of the glories of our democratic way, is always in danger of being lost to sight. We are accustomed to dealing with atoms and dollars and votes, all standardized units, each identical with the rest of its kind, and are tempted to treat men in the same way. It is true that human diversity greatly increases the problems of the biologist, sociologist, historian and politician, but it saves us from the shuddering nightmare of life in a community where everybody is like everybody else, or where people have been turned out in only a limited number of models. The interplay between individuals endowed with this enormous range of genetic diversity gives life its dramatic interest.

The existence of individuals in the human species poses some of the most profound philosophical questions that we have to face. These begin with the basic issue of the *self,* that integrating center of the individual, that binds all aspects of it together. Is there really such a thing, and if so, what is it? Does it control behavior? Are there values connected with it that we ought to recognize? These simple questions involve important problems in biology, psychology and philosophy. It is significant, I think, that just as there is no appropriate place in biological theory into which the phenomenon of organization can be fitted, so modern psychology seems to have no place for a concept of the self. These two phenomena of biological and psychological integration are closely related, and to discuss the nature of one will certainly involve the other.

Much of modern psychology regards everything that happens to a person as initiated from the outside and not as arising spontaneously from within. It is environment that is most important, not heredity. The human individual at its beginning is a *tabula rasa,* a clean slate, on which is to be written the record of its experiences, and it is these that chiefly determine what it does. Memories built into the substance of the brain accumulate, associations are built up, and there is much complex, regulatory activity; but there seems to be no place in this process for a permanent, integrative factor like the "self" to hold these things together as a unity.

If one is not committed to such a theory, however, one finds something very different from this. The individual one sees is not a fluid and indeterminate thing, molded by the world it lives in, but has a surprisingly stubborn and permanent core of its own around which its activities all center. This knot of norms, steady states, potencies and purposes of which it is composed is almost impossible to loosen. It can be killed, or its course directed in minor ways; but to break it down and make it into something different, to shake it free from its past, to destroy its identity—this the organized pattern of individuality successfully resists. As a man I am the same person that I was as a boy though my body is almost completely different and the content of my brain greatly altered. The central pattern of me has not been obliterated by altered circumstances. I still remain *myself.* It is hard to see how a series of reflexes alone could produce this constancy. The self has a history that is not a mere repetition of reactions. It maintains its own identity. "Like the universe as a whole," says Bergson, "like each conscious being taken separately, the organism which lives is a thing that *endures.* Its past, in its entirety, is prolonged into its present and abides there, actual and acting."[1] How can any mere aggregation of material particles do this, I ask. One configuration might succeed another, but to maintain the continuity of an identical whole requires the action of something that binds together gene action, conditioning, memories and all the complexities of the past into a constant unity. For this we need invoke no vague, hypothetical self, for there is a specific, living, protoplasmic pattern for each individual that channels the behavior of the organism into a constant course, much as the matter and energy of its body are channeled into a unity in its organized development. What this pattern is and how it operates is a major problem of biology and psychology. To call it a homeostatic process is merely to give it a name. To say it is simply a group of genes is to oversimplify it.

Objections to the concept of a self have often been raised. No mechanism for it has been discovered any more than for biological organization in general. It is so easy to assume its existence and by this means "explain" what a person does without really accounting for it at all, that the modern science of behavior has usually abandoned the concept of a self altogether. In recent years, however, some psychologists are beginning to recognize the self as a necessary part of the human individual, difficult though it still is to explain in scientific terms. "For two generations," says Professor Allport, "psychologists have tried every conceivable way of accounting for the integration, organization

---

[1] Henri Bergson, *Creative Evolution,* trans. by Arthur Mitchell, 1911, p. 15.

and striving of the human person without having recourse
to the postulate of a self." In a vigorous plea for recognition of a self in process of becoming, he states his belief
that "an adequate psychology of becoming cannot be written exclusively in terms of stimulus, emotional excitement,
association and response. It requires subjective and inner
principles of organization of the sort frequently designated
by the terms self or ego. Whether these labels are employed
is less important than that the principles they imply be
fully admitted in accounting for the development of personality."[2]

Is the self, I ask, purely a human problem? In many of
the higher animals something much like it is often to be
seen. We have all known dogs that had their own peculiar
dispositions, loves and loyalties, and it would be hard to
deny each of them some attributes of a self. If this word is
to be meaningful, however, something more must be im-
plied by it, and this something belongs to man alone. Man
seems to have been the first animal to *recognize* his selfhood; to step outside himself, as it were, and comprehend
his existence as a distinct individual. Not until this happened did the "I" stand apart from the "Thou" and the
"It," to use Martin Buber's words, or did questions about
himself begin to trouble him. The recognition of his own
identity as something different from the rest of the world
was one thing that made the ape-man human. Consciousness was not involved in this advance, for certainly the
higher animals are conscious of their surroundings and
their own sensations. It was not until *self*-consciousness

---

[2] Gordon W. Allport, *Becoming*, 1955, pp. 37, 60.

evolved, with all this meant, that the self was really born.

But the self is turning out to be a much more complex thing than a mere string to hold the individual together. There is evidence that it has an organized pattern and a wholeness just as does the body. It is not only a conscious entity but reaches into the depths of the unconscious as well. The significance of this part of a person was stressed by Freud many years ago, who showed that below the ordinary conscious level of man's life there is an important part of him that only rarely rises into focal consciousness but that has an important influence on his behavior. In it, said Freud, are stored youthful experiences, repressions, feelings of guilt and much else that normally is inhibited, and these things are responsible for many of the mind's ills. This concept of the unconscious, from which has grown the practice of psychoanalysis, has been concerned chiefly with the pathological side of the mind. Modern students of this *depth psychology,* however, notably Jung, Rank, Progoff and Maslow, have examined particularly the normal, nonpathological character of this deep self and sought there a knowledge of the basic formative patterns and tendencies in man, a picture of his *wholeness in depth,* qualities deeply implanted in his nature. Much is said nowadays about the importance of self-realization or self-actualization, the free development of the potentialities of the individual. This is important, but even more so is to make the self worth realizing.

Such a concept of the self as a complex whole leads to the next higher aspect of the organizing capacity of living stuff, *personality*. A human being is a treasure house of possibilities, directives and ideals, but these mean little unless they are fulfilled. They reach fruition, for good or ill, in a *person*. A person is a developed self, an individual in whom some of the potencies and tendencies of the self are realized. Human personality is at a level so much higher than mere protoplasmic organization that it is hard to think of the two as basically the same; but we shall understand man better, I believe, if we recognize that both, indeed, *are* expressions of the same integrative processes of life. We are acquainted with personality in our friends and have a vivid inner experience of it in ourselves. It is so rich and various and so obviously the highest flowering of the human organism that it seems far more than a series of mere reflexes. Says Sir Julian Huxley of it: "This primacy of human personality has been, in different ways, a *postulate* both of Christianity and of liberal democracy; but it is a *fact* of evolution. By whatever objective standard we choose to take, properly developed human personalities are the highest products of evolution; they have greater capacities and have reached a higher level of organization than any other parts of the world substance."[3]

The very fact of separateness between personalities engenders a sense of individual value, I believe, that would be impossible in bits of a continuous living mass. The feeling I possess of my own personality as I face my individual responsibilities and destiny has in it the very flavor of reality. It is only in persons that ideas are born, by persons that discoveries are made and poems written. It is only as persons that we can communicate with one another, and this may be the only way we can finally make contact

[3] *Evolution in Action*, 1953, p. 165.

with the universe itself. I can learn something of the phenomenon of biological individuality by direct inner experience of it at its highest level which no amount of objective study of animals or man could ever give. Perhaps life is ultimately understandable only in terms of personality. The significant fact is that personality has a firm biological basis.

Because personality does not fit into the pattern of modern psychology, that science has rather little to say about it. This is regrettable, and even as laymen we are inclined to agree with Allport when he gently chides his colleagues: "It is especially in relation to the formation and development of human personality that we need to open doors. For it is precisely here that our ignorance and uncertainty are greatest. Our methods, however well suited to the study of sensory processes, animal research, and pathology, are not fully adequate; and interpretations arising from the exclusive use of these methods are stultifying. Some theories of becoming are based largely on behavior of sick and anxious people or upon the antics of captive and desperate rats. Fewer theories have derived from the study of healthy human beings, those who strive not so much to preserve life as to make it worth living. Thus we find today many studies of criminals, few of law-abiders; many of fear, few of courage; more on hostility than on affiliation; much on the blindness in man, little on his vision; much on his past, little on his outreaching into the future."[4]

Important as the individual person is, we must remem-

---

[4] Allport, *op. cit.*, p. 18.

ber that creation does not end with him alone. He cannot live without others. Man is a part of the greater organism, society, much as a cell is part of the body, and he has obligations to it. Selfishness is glorification of the self. Without it man could not have survived, but the great problem of morals now is to balance fairly a natural concern for ourselves with an equal concern for others. Self and society are the poles of human life.

If one accepts the idea that the unity of the human individual, as a continuing personality, is an expression of the organizing power of life, he must ask the final question: may this integration be carried one step further and help interpret for us the concept of what is called the *soul?* Is the richness and depth of personality part of a still higher unity, the *essential* person, something that may even be significant in the universe itself, a man's peculiar treasure and perhaps his very passport to eternity? Here the discussion touches a vital point in the construction of a religious philosophy, for the soul is one of the great affirmations of religion. To save it from perdition has been the chief task of many faiths. Anguished concern over its salvation long distinguished the life of each believer, drawing his attention from this world to the next. In recent days, however, religion has much less to say about the soul, and even in Christianity the concern for its welfare felt by our grandfathers has remained chiefly in Roman Catholicism and Protestant fundamentalism. The reason for this, aside from the growing secularism of our time, is that the concept of the soul is very difficult for modern man to grasp. If even the self does not find a place in our psychology, the idea of the soul is far more foreign still.

Merely to use the word, save as a figure of speech, marks one as almost outside the pale of ideological respectability. Where in the body, one may ask, is it to be found? In the pineal gland, perhaps? How can it ever be "lost"? The only logical thing to do about the soul, say many, is to throw out the whole idea as mystical moonshine and accept the fact that there is nothing in man beyond the living mechanism of his body.

But a generation that has seen the revolution in modern physics and learned to accept without a shock such ideas as that an electron may occupy two places at once, or that matter may be created, hesitates to say that anything is *necessarily* possible or impossible, sensible or senseless. There are more things in heaven and earth, even today, than are dreamed of in our philosophies. Man's way of thinking about the universe has undergone a radical change and his mind is more open as he approaches such questions as that of the soul. *Something* pulls the human individual together as a unity, and whether we call this ego, self, personality or soul seems but a difference in emphasis. Soul is human personality writ large and invested with eternal values. It is nothing new, I think, suddenly injected into man, but the fulfillment of the possibilities latent in the first germ of life. What eternal qualities it may have gained in this progression is one of the major problems of human nature. Just what the soul is we shall never know until we can answer the simpler biological problem of what draws matter into an organized system and makes it live.

This conception is opposed to the orthodox Hebrew and Christian idea of the soul, which thinks of it as something distinctively human, breathed into man at the Creation and marking him off sharply from the brutes. To regard it as the culmination of the processes and possibilities of all life, however, seems to me a higher concept than to think of it as miraculously introduced into the body. If we accept the ancient view, we must face the very difficult question as to when and where in man's ancestral line the soul first appeared, just as we have to face essentially the same question in deciding where first the primate stock produced a man. I am sure that fundamentalist theologians, could they have been there, would have been perplexed to know just where the soulless ape came to have a soul. The church of Rome, though admitting (with caution) that man's body is the product of evolutionary change, denies this for his soul. It maintains that somewhere in the past the first soul was *created,* just as somewhere (though just where and when is not clear) the soul comes into being in the development of the human embryo. But this is not the way that nature works. The great lesson men have learned from the concept of evolution is that life progresses slowly, gradually, and not by sudden jumps. It follows nature's leisurely method of bringing things to pass. The human being, with his distinctive attributes of mind and soul, whatever these turn out to be, is the flowering of something that began long ago when these would not have been recognized as what we call them now. One may object, of course, that an oak tree does not have a mind or an elephant a soul, but in these organisms reside the germs from which, along another evolutionary line than theirs, these higher qualities have been developed. Let us not forget that a new-born baby cannot do most of the things he does so easily when he is grown. A fertilized human egg is still farther back on the same developmental road. Neither of these small organisms do we undervalue, for we recognize in them the possibility of something higher. In every living thing the germ exists of such development, though the upward evolutionary pathway to its fulfillment may be blocked.

In our Western tradition, each of us has his own soul, distinct from all the others. This is opposed to some Eastern philosophies, which regard the apparent plurality of souls as illusion, a series of different aspects of the same thing. They believe that the individual soul at death loses itself in the great spiritual reservoir of the universe. The very concept of personality is a Western, not an Eastern, one. How this fundamental difference can be resolved I find it hard to see.

One more question must be asked, implicit in all the rest, about this thing we call the soul: What relation does it have to the body in which it is expressed? I will shortly present arguments for the fundamental similarity of the *physical* and the *psychical* in man, discovering in both the same integrating and purposive character so evident in all life. They are, I believe, coequal; two aspects of the same living system, with a common origin in the organizing character of living stuff. If this is true, the psychical side of man has as much logical claim to reality as does the body. The craftsman's pattern—existing perhaps only in his mind—on which a machine is built and to which its construction must conform is as real as the machine itself. The protoplasmic pattern that directs the development of the individual as an organized whole comes, so to speak, out of the creative activity of the universe and may have a higher claim to significance than the body it controls.

If the mind, or soul—whatever it is—can organize images and ideas in the brain and in the depths of the unconscious, is it not to be regarded as much like that which directs the organized development of the body? It is unreasonable to segregate the organizing process into several different functions. One may better assume that in *every* aspect of life—physical and psychical—there is a persistent tendency toward organization, wholeness, end-seeking; and that this manifests itself in various ways. The soul may therefore be regarded as the same *sort* of thing that governs the growth and functioning of the body. Soul and body are intimately related. A materialist regards the body as the basic reality that dominates and directs the "soul," but one may well argue that it is the other way around and that the physical is not the precursor of the psychical, but actually its product! It was Charles Kingsley, I believe, who suggested that the soul secretes the body as a clam its shell. This you will say is simply poetic license; but biologically, body and mind are closely knit, and so are body and soul. Something guides the disposition of matter and energy in the organism, something not yet understood and seemingly different from anything else in nature. On the question as to what it is, my whole argument depends.

In *all* life, from bacteria to man, one can see the same self-regulatory process of integration. To understand it fully at one level would tell us much about it at the others. Tennyson's insight was profound when he said that if we knew *all* about the flower in the crannied wall, there would be little left that we should need to know. Life is life, basically the same from bottom to top. The fact that this thread of organized development runs through it everywhere simplifies the task of understanding man, for all our problems finally come down to this one: the organizing, formative, creative power of life. This problem is so formidable, however, that to solve it we may have to wait until better methods of attacking it have been discovered. Despite the confident words they sometimes use and the great discoveries that they have made, biologists in all humility must admit that little progress toward its scientific solution has been made. The nature of this organizing process is of vital consequence for any philosophy. Today this great fact is unexplained, and the very foundations of biology thus are still uncertain. We must accept the fact, however, and not ignore it, and must press on to the solution of the problems that it raises. The organizing and integrating capacity of life provides the inclusive religious philosophy we seek with something tangible on which it can anchor the concept of the soul, something in which the intimate relationship of matter and mind is clear. This is an important step toward our goal of a unified belief. The soul is a magnificent hypothesis, and until we know more about the unsolved problems that cluster around every living thing, we should hesitate before insisting dogmatically that it is nothing but an empty and discredited superstition. It is an important part of the great bridge of life that we are trying here to build.

VI
FROM LIFE TO MIND

WHAT MAKES A MAN SO much more diffi-
cult to understand than a machine is that he leads a curiously double life; not double in the sense that I have
discussed before, of being partly a thinking and partly a
desiring creature, but double in quite a different fashion. To
the physiologist he is a material system that must be
studied quite objectively, like any complex mechanism.
Science examines him from the outside, as if he were on a
laboratory table, and thus gains knowledge of him that is
uninfluenced by prejudice or emotion. The man himself,
however, is sure that much more than machinery is there.
Whatever he may call it—mind or spirit, soul or psyche
—this maze of tissues seems to be *inhabited* by something.
To discover by direct inner experience what this is like
was once the province of psychology. Such methods are
outmoded now because the facts discovered in this way
seemed too uncertain and influenced too much by circumstance to be reliable. Science shuts its eyes and pretends
that there is *nothing* there but protoplasmic mechanisms.
Nevertheless, the man inside feels vividly that in some

fashion, strange but very real, he permeates his body, and that its behavior is under his direction and control. His feelings of selfhood and freedom are so strong that, in his psychological innocence, he finds it hard to believe that he is no more at last than a collection of molecules and a succession of reflex acts. Here is our problem, posed in simple terms: what is the relation between the material body, on the one hand, and, on the other, a hypothetical something else—clearly immaterial, perhaps nonexistent, but possibly quite real and more significant than anything else on earth? This is the fundamental question we must try to answer if we are ever to bring into harmony the two opposed philosophies about which men are now divided.

The relation between mind and body is a question that for centuries has troubled common men and great philosophers. The issue in our time is complicated by the fact that many psychologists refuse to admit the existence of "mind" at all. This word, they say, is simply a shorthand expression for behavior, activity, the things we do; but to many, this behaviorism seems an oversimplification of a very complex matter.

Various ways have been suggested to account for the body-mind relationship. A familiar one is the dualism of Descartes and others, which assumes that body and mind are entirely separate things, coexisting for a while in man. This meets with obvious difficulties. Most people dislike dualism in their philosophy and hope to find an underlying unity in things, a monism of some sort. One such monism is reached by the materialist, who sees in matter the essence of reality and looks on mind as merely a by-product of natural processes that go on in the body. The man of faith, on the contrary, finds his unity in the spiritual forces of the universe, to which matter and the rest of the "natural" world are subordinate. The psychical qualities of man are among these forces. Both types of monism have the disadvantage that in each of them one important aspect of a man must be regarded as of no final consequence. I believe it is possible to find a monism that leaves both intact.

Man's psychical qualities—thinking, feeling and the processes that determine behavior—seem to be aspects of the whole organism which he is, not of its separate parts or any of its particular metabolic activities. This suggests a relation between biological organization and psychical activity, and makes it possible to interpret the latter in terms of the former. To find, if possible, the roots of mind and spirit in a fundamental biological activity will be of great importance for our task of building a bridge between material and spiritual qualities. This to me has always been an attractive idea and I have tried to develop it in earlier publications (see page 252). In the previous chapter we have seen how one tendency in biological organization—the production of single individual organisms—may be the basis, in man, for the self, personality and even its extension as the soul. I should now like to suggest how the other tendency—the continued progression of the organism, in its development, toward a precise end—may be the basis for desire, purpose and man's higher psychical traits, culminating in thought itself. This is an idea so radical that it seems to some people quite unrealistic and impossible. Much can be said for it, however, and my whole argument in the present book is based upon it. Since some may find this difficult to understand in a single piece, I have broken it up into a series of separate statements for greater clarity.

Bodily development is a controlled progression from egg to maturity, so regulated at every step that a precise end is reached.

This progression toward an end is evident not only in normal development but also when this is disrupted (see page 98), for the organism, as we have seen, shows a remarkable ability in such cases to restore itself and so to regulate its activity that it returns to its typical course. As a living thing moves forward from stage to stage in its developmental cycle it preserves its individuality but never settles down to the static condition of a machine, which would be death. It is continually moving *toward* something; rapidly in early development or more slowly as it nears maturity, and it regulates its course with precision. It does not change in a random or aimless fashion. The end to which it moves is the result of interaction between genes and environment, but it is a controlled and precisely directed process.

Regulation implies the presence of something to which development conforms—a norm or goal immanent in the organism.

The living system from its start is "set," so to speak, in such a way that a particular course is followed. There is something in it that foreshadows the developmental program from the egg toward the adult individual, somewhat as the pattern on a phonograph record foreshadows the music that will be produced as the needle moves over it from beginning to end. This pattern or norm must be represented in some way in the living stuff of the cells. In every cell, furthermore, each of the thousands of genes must be activated in a particular order, degree and direction if the embryo is to develop in a specific way. The norm involves a relationship among the genes, a pattern of some sort in the cell. The character of this norm is still quite unknown.

This regulation to ends is evident not only in bodily development (embryology) but in behavior.

The essential step in my argument is that the phenomenon of organization also underlies the psychical side of man's life. It can be shown, I think, that there is no very sharp distinction between the *development* of the body and its *behavior,* between an embryonic and an instinctive activity. Both conform to norms in living stuff. In many simple animals which are active from their earliest stages, development and behavior occur together from the first. Even when the embryo is inactive during early growth, as in birds and mammals, it is hard to separate the two processes. Where, in the hatching egg, does embryology end and behavior begin? When the chick, with a peck of its beak, breaks the shell, we call this behavior, an instinctive act; but how does it differ, in essence, from earlier movements of the growing embryo that lead up to it? Furthermore, behavior much like the constructive activities of development sometimes takes place long after embryonic growth is over. A bird, for example, builds a nest so precisely formed that a naturalist can identify the builder by his work as well as by his bodily structure. Behavior is morphogenetic. Development and behavior are simultaneous activities of living organisms. Development is

chiefly limited to the growth and unfolding of the embryo
to the adult, whereas behavior involves the activity of the
whole body or of its parts and lasts through life.

*Goal-seeking in behavior is more complex than in em-
bryology. It may not follow a single course, but be directed
temporarily to subordinate goals.*

In development, goal-seeking is usually a single-track
process from egg to adult; in behavior, there may be many
successive goals. In a fly-catching bird, for example, the
main goal is a full stomach but secondary ones are the
seizure of any insects that come near. These goals change,
but always against the background of the fundamental
one of getting food. This long-term goal alters as the bird
goes through its cycle of mating, nest-building, feeding
young and migrating. Underneath all these is the basic
goal of successful survival.

The difference between the two types of goal-seeking
(developmental and behavioral) seems great but actually
it is not. In both, the reaction between genes and environment determines what the norm will be. Environmental
factors influencing *development* are relatively few and are
necessarily slow in their effect. In butterflies, the color
and pattern of the wings and, in fruit flies, the wing vena-
tion (and many other traits), are modified by the temperature at which the organism develops. The norm is different
under different conditions. *Behavior* is also affected by
environmental factors, though much more conspicuously.
If an animal finds its surroundings too hot or too cold, too
light or too dark for its comfort, it will move to a better
spot; if it is hungry, it will seek food; if a predator
threatens, it will hide or run; if a mate calls, it will move to

her side. To its behavioral norms it adjusts its activities
in such a way that favorable conditions for its life are
maintained.

In controlling behavior an animal depends on its sense
organs. Environmental factors (stimuli) sensed by these
call forth specific muscular responses and thus determine
what it does. These organs are responsive to a great number of stimuli and, in an animal that moves about, the
direction, intensity and variety of these stimuli are very
numerous. An insect-catching bird may see an insect, and
to make its behavior conform to a norm set up in its nervous system it will fly toward the insect and capture it. A
rather limited number of norms but a great variety of
stimuli will thus result in a very wide range of behavior. In
short, typical behavior of a motile animal is varied because
it must continually regulate itself in conformity to norms
in its nervous system. The principle is the same as in the
regulatory goal-seeking of bodily development, but in behavior the effective environmental stimuli are much more
numerous and reaction to them is much more rapid and
varied.

*Behavioral norms, like developmental ones, presumably
are represented by protoplasmic patterns, chiefly in the
cells of the brain.*

What a behavioral norm may be, physically, is quite unknown. I see no reason to think, however, that it is *basically* different from the developmental one in the egg and
other cells that guides the unfolding of the organism. It is
probably a chemical or physical pattern or field in living
stuff. The conclusion that a behavioral norm is a pattern
set up in the nervous system, presumably by gene action

and natural selection, is strongly suggested by a study of some remarkable animal instincts. The web of a spider, for example, is so precisely formed that a knowledgeable arachnologist can name the species by its web alone. *Something* corresponding to the pattern of the web, something that I have here been calling a norm, must evidently be present in the spider's brain. When what is distinctive is an *act,* with no material result, this, too, must be foreshadowed in the brain. A remarkable example of such a norm is found in migratory birds. Most migration is at night and in many cases appears to be guided by the stars. This fact has been checked by releasing migrating birds in a planetarium that has been rotated somewhat from its normal relation to the heavenly bodies. In such cases the birds will orient themselves, and begin brief flights, in conformity to the position of the stars in the planetarium rather than to those in the sky, which they cannot see. In the bird's brain there seems to be something that serves as a map of at least the major stars and that guides behavior. This gives striking support to the idea that there *is* a physical pattern in the nervous system which is the basis of behavioral norms.

A behavioral goal often persists even if conditions change. It may be reached by very different paths, as in the cases of equifinality in bodily development (see page 98). The conditions that confront a bird in building its nest are different in every case. No two locations are exactly alike, and the sources of material are different. What gives unity to the task despite these variables is the constant direction of behavior to a particular end, the building of a nest. This behavior is resourceful, not because the bird meets the problems intelligently (it performs the task as well the first time as the tenth) but because in some way the image of a nest seems to be implanted in the cells of the brain. The image directs the various details of the bird's behavior, and under various conditions, to the accomplishment of the end of building a nest. This involves more than a linear series of steps, each determined by the one before it. Something—the goal to be reached, the image of a nest—coordinates the whole program of behavior. The acts may be different in detail but the goal is the same.[1]

That there are patterns in the brain is also suggested by the facts of Gestalt psychology. In looking at a confused and apparently random set of lines, a person will often suddenly recognize order there and see the form of a familiar object. The millions of individual impulses from retina to brain are somehow pulled together into an orderly system, much as a "scrambled" telephone message is "unscrambled" at the other end. The mind decodes the jumble of sensations and organizes them. It perceives in patterns.

Behavioral norms in the brain govern responses to stimuli in conformity to these norms. Behavior is therefore more than simple reflex action.

The behavioral response made to a stimulus from a sense organ, if my suggestion is correct, is not a direct one (stimulus → response) but is indirect. Between stimulus and response is a third element, the norm set up in the

[1] This idea has been well developed by W. E. Agar in his book *A Contribution to the Theory of the Living Organism,* 2d ed., 1951, esp. p. 21.

brain cells (stimulus → norm → response). The response conforms to the norm presumably by a feedback process that keeps behavior pointed in such a direction that it will fulfill the requirements of the norm. Such behavior may sometimes be a bewilderingly rapid series of goal-seeking acts (conformities to norms) as in men playing tennis, but they are goal-seekings, nevertheless, and fundamentally, I believe, similar to other biological ones. The brain is like a clearinghouse, receiving stimuli from the environment and governing the behavioral responses that are made to these *in conformity to goals set up in it.* Such behavior is more than reflex action, more than an act determined directly by a stimulus, for responses to the same stimulus differ as the norms change.

Directiveness toward ends is experienced as a desire, and then as a purpose, so that psychical life is the sense of being consciously oriented toward ends.

The essence of my suggestion as to the relation of the physical to the psychical comes down to this: If there is in the brain a pattern or norm in conformity to which behavior is directed to certain ends, it is logical to expect *that this directiveness itself should be felt,* as by something like a kinesthetic sense. I believe it can be, and that the feeling of being oriented or drawn toward some end is the origin of the sensation of *desiring* or *wanting* it. Desire, at bottom, is the same sort of biological orientation evident in the far simpler directiveness of bodily development, but it is subjectively *experienced.* Wanting, desiring, craving (and their opposites) are emotions. In the simplest cases they lead to action. If one wants something, one naturally tries to take or use or enjoy it, so that beyond the sense

of wanting there is the added feeling of intent or purpose.[2]
Just as a structure, yet to be developed, may be said to be
immanent in the cells of the embryo, so a purpose, yet to
be realized, may be said to be immanent in the cells of the
brain. Purpose is the potentially active element in the experience of biological directiveness or goal-seeking. It may
be fulfilled in a bodily act of behavior or in a mental act—
an intention or a thought or an idea.

The purposeful brain resembles a purposeful machine,
such as a computer. When one of these has been "programmed" and is ready to begin its work, the answer to

---

[2] The word "purpose" is in disrepute biologically since it is believed by many to imply teleology, the influence of mind on matter
and of the future on the present. It may be interpreted quite
mechanically, however, for it simply recognizes the presence in a
system of something that guides the activities of that system in conformity to a particular norm set up in it, as in a feedback mechanism. Thus a thermostat may be constructed in such a way that it
has a "purpose" to maintain a temperature of 70°. There is in it
no violation of natural law, no "final" cause. What has made the
concept of purpose unpopular in biology is that careless teaching
has given many people the idea that a plant or animal, by its very
nature, will do what is best for it; that it tries, purposefully, to
behave in the way that will cause it to survive. Thus roots are
sometimes said to grow downward "for the purpose" of getting
water, and birds to fly south in the fall "so that" they will avoid the
winter. This is obviously untrue. The beautiful adaptations of
organisms, both in structure and behavior, are natural only in the
sense that they are the results of natural selection. Most behavioral
norms, to be sure, produce action favorable to the organism, but
this is simply because all others have been eliminated by selection.
A bird with a norm that caused it to migrate northward in the
fall would have a short expectancy of life.

the question asked of it is immanent, so to speak, in the particular pattern or norm now established in the computer's mechanism, and will be reached by a series of consecutive steps. This resemblance is so close that many psychologists believe the brain itself can be studied most fruitfully on the hypothesis that its essential character is indeed like that of a computer. The brain is much more, however, than a mechanism which receives a stimulus and produces a behavioral result. We have seen how a developmental norm may persist and be effective even when conditions radically change, as in the experiment with the sponge. Similarly, a behavioral norm persists, even when outer conditions change. The individual stays on the track, directed toward an end. If a computer could be subjected to greatly altered conditions, in its outer or inner environment, and still, by a sort of mechanical regeneration, could produce the same answer as before, its resemblance to the brain would be still closer. If the computer could *experience* the state of its inner, directive mechanical pattern, the suggestion is not too bizarre, I think, that this pattern of immanent action, to which the busy mechanism will conform, would be *felt* as what in man we call a desire or purpose or idea.

Psychical activity seems to be limited to living matter.

Against the suggestion I have here presented, objection will be raised that if desire and purpose are the subjective experience of the regulatory activities of a biological mechanism, the organism, why should not other regulatory mechanisms, also, have a subjective, purposeful accompaniment? What is there about a machine made of protein, water, DNA and a few other specific substances that should give it the capacity to bring forth such qualities as desire, purpose, thought and other phenomena that we call mental, whereas machines made of metal lack this capacity? Perhaps the panpsychists are right, and there is a glimmering of the psyche in *all* matter. Whitehead has suggested that atoms are organisms, though on a very minute scale. They certainly are organized systems. It may be that mind *is* in everything, though we can recognize it easily only in extraordinarily complex systems like the brain. This is far more complicated than any computer yet made. It is conceivable that the super-computers men are likely to be building a hundred years from now *may* show evidence of thought and feeling. Science fiction has made us receptive to all sorts of novel ideas, and this one might not seem so foolish to our great-grandchildren.

Mental phenomena, however, in any meaningful sense of the word, seem to be related to *living* matter. Atoms may be "organisms" in a sense but only by analogy and not as real kin to any microorganisms that we know, even the tiniest of viruses. The relation between the psychical and the physical will, I think, turn out to be an aspect of the relation between the living and the lifeless. There is something more in protoplasm than mere mechanics that makes it the seat of psychical processes. When we discover the physical basis of a living organism we shall find the secret of its psyche, too.

Consciousness involves an element of directiveness.

Underneath these questions is the basic problem of *consciousness,* manifest in life at its highest levels and most acutely in man. An organism, and the human one most of all, differs radically from a machine in one respect that has always complicated any study of the psychical life. Man has a subjective side. He is *conscious* and can *feel*. Much of what he feels comes through the stimulation of his sense organs by factors in the environment. Through these organs he maintains contact with the world around him and reacts to changes there in a regulatory fashion. He adapts himself to them. A mechanism can do this, too, but (unless we are gravely mistaken) it is not conscious of the impact upon it of these outer influences, or of its control of the changes it undergoes. The most sensitive photographic emulsion, able to register minute differences in quality and intensity of light upon a film and to record there a faithful picture of the world outside, does not *see*. The sensitivity that eye and brain possess, so similar to that of lens and film, is translated in some unknown fashion into conscious *feeling*. We are each inside a living organism, an amazingly coordinated protoplasmic system, and this intimate contact gives us a different sort of relation to the world from that which any mechanism can possess. It may be, as we have said before, that only through this inner conscious experience of living can we discover what life really is. The fact that a mechanism does not feel is the major difference between a machine and an organism, a difference that lies at the bottom of our problems in biological philosophy.

There is no agreement as to the significance or even the existence of consciousness. The more extreme behaviorists, among psychologists, deny not only that consciousness has any effect on behavior but even that it really exists at all. They regard it as a sort of epiphenomenon, a product of the physical changes taking place in the tissues of the brain.

Thought, to them, is "subvocal articulation," minute motions of the larynx that accompany unspoken words. Others accept consciousness as real but believe it is simply a psychological correlate of changes in the brain and has no significance in producing these changes. For such psychologists, the wide gamut of human feelings—pleasure and pain; fear, anxiety and remorse; desire and its many aspects, and all the other manifestations of that stirring in the brain cells that we call consciousness—are all ineffective on human conduct and, as far as man is concerned, are essentially without significance. This is a field of controversy in psychology today into which a layman would be rash to enter. There are many psychologists and philosophers, however, who believe that consciousness is real, by any reasonable test for reality, and that conscious states do have some part in determining behavior.

Such people, however, are still troubled by the difficulty that behaviorism has tried to avoid. They must answer the ancient problem of how matter and mind are related, of how physical events are translated into mental ones. Here, perhaps, the suggestions I have been discussing may be worth considering. A general awareness of the environment is presumably a quality of every living thing, since all protoplasm is sensitive to stimulation. Consciousness, however, seems to be more than mere awareness or sensation. It represents an *involvement of the organism with the environment* in the sense that the organism is continually endeavoring, so to speak, to maintain a particular state of its activity under the conditions where it is. At its highest levels, as we know it in man, conscious awareness is therefore accompanied by at least some degree of wanting or desiring. Whenever he is awake, there is always something that man seeks, even though this is only to stay the way he is. That consciousness is thus to be considered not as a passive but as an active condition gives it a clearly biological character. It is an awareness of being alive and thus, necessarily, of wanting something.

If the essential quality of living is regulation or directiveness to *ends,* and if consciousness is real, the hypothesis seems reasonable that this directiveness should be consciously experienced as I have suggested, and that *this is what desire and purpose are.* Such an idea does not *explain* a psychical fact in terms of a physical one, or vice versa. It simply calls attention to the similarity between two very different phenomena which suggests that a relation of some sort exists between them. We may compare this to the relation between a magnetic field and a steel rod that is lying in it. In living stuff, and notably that of the brain, there is what we may call a *biological field* related to the physical and chemical activities of the brain substance. Which is cause and which effect is by no means clear, and there are metaphysical problems involved. In the great uncertainty that still surrounds the psychophysical relationship, the suggestion that has been made here is entitled to consideration. It involves neither mysticism nor vitalism, as some have maintained, but is simply an attempt to relate widely different facts in an orderly fashion.

Thought is basically purposive.

Mental images, things "seen" although they do not physically exist, and products of the imagination generally, have always been difficult for behaviorism to explain. If there *is* a normative pattern in the brain, however, a Gestalt of some sort under an individual's control, this may be experienced in consciousness as an image, just as I have suggested that any norm may be. It usually does not lead to action but resembles what we call a *thought*. Indeed, conscious thought, in our states of meditation or deliberation, seems to be a succession of such images which do not translate themselves into behavior. Thought may therefore be regarded as fundamentally purposive. William James once remarked that no actions but such as are done for an end are indubitable expressions of mind.

As memory and imagination grew and language was perfected, men became able to think in abstract terms. They learned to recognize general facts and to relate particular ones to these and so to reason. Thus man's intellect, like his purposiveness, can be interpreted as an aspect of the directive, end-seeking character of life.

What, then, shall we conclude as to the relation of biological organization to the nature of *mind?* Is there actually in man (or any other living thing) anything that can rightfully be called by this name, or is mind nothing more than a shorthand expression for behavior? I believe that a good argument can be presented for the existence of mind in its own right, as a biological fact. If emotions and purposes, the fundamental psychical phenomena, are experiences of a goal-seeking directiveness inside the organism and are not simply responses to stimuli from without, this gives objective reality to a continuing inner control of vital activities that is worthy to be called "mind." I may thus venture to define mind as *whatever in a living system sets up a continuing series of norms in conformity to which are directed the activities of the individual.* This definition is so broad that it is not very useful for psychology. For man we may shorten it to *whatever sets up norms in the brain to which behavior conforms.*

Mind, by such a definition, is by no means limited to man but can be found, at least in its simplest elements, in every living thing. The triumphs of man's intellect have their origin, I think, at the roots of the ascending evolutionary tree and are a manifestation of the basic regulatory character of all life. Here it is that mind and matter meet in the unity of the organism.

The suggestion here presented has not received wide support from biologists; partly, I suspect, because many have not understood it clearly, and partly because it may seem to remove mental activity from the control of physical determinism. It has two important advantages, however: (1) it provides what seems to me a reasonable interpretation of the body-mind problem by identifying it with that of biological organization, a question more open to direct study, and thus hopefully provides a possible basis for reconciliation between the religious and the materialistic attitudes; and (2) it provides a biological foundation for the interpretation of values, perhaps the key problem in the study of man. I have not tried to "explain" mind or values in material terms but simply have pointed out that two sets of facts, one biological and the other psychological, are similar enough to suggest that they have a common source and presumably a common nature, both growing out of regulatory activities in the human organism.

The problem of causation in the brain, and especially of the relation between physical events there and "mental" events, still is far from solution. The pattern or norm in the brain, on which I believe a behavioral or a mental act is based, doubtless has a physical correlate. What this is and how it is determined is essentially the biological problem of organism.[3]

Motivation

Modern psychology, taking its cue from physiology, interprets the motivation behind behavioral acts as the direct result of the application of energy to the bodily mechanism through a series of chemical and physical changes. It regards behavior as the result of propulsions or drives, just as one does the movement of a car. A "hunger drive" pushes a man toward food, or a "sex drive" toward sexual satisfaction. At higher levels are the drives for power, fame, social position and many other things, but they are

---

[3] The resemblance between development and behavior has been recognized by other biologists, though no one, I think, has carried the implications of this quite as far as I have tried to do. E. S. Russell remarks: "Morphogenetic activities and instinctive activities are linked, complementary and functionally equivalent, and resemble one another in their essential characteristics" (The Directiveness of Organic Activities, 1945, p. 181). Says Ralph Lillie: "In living organisms physical integration and psychical integration represent two aspects, corresponding to two mutually complementary sets of factors, of one and the same biological process" (General Biology and Philosophy of Organism, 1945, p. 46). J. C. Smuts has said: "Mind is thus the direct descendant of organic regulation and carries forward the same task" (Holism and Evolution, 1926, p. 224).

all interpreted as drives. The important question is, what does the steering? Modern psychology says this is the result of forces that push a man along in directions presumably determined in some way by events in his brain cells, though just how this is done is by no means clear. It usually explains the sense of desiring or purposing as the result of a *tension* set up in the brain, which can be *reduced* by appropriate behavior. But to produce a precise sequence of behavior by this means would require, I should think, as precise a pattern of tension reduction in the brain as the pattern which I suggest occurs there when a behavioral norm is set up. One process is as hard to understand as the other.

The conception developed in this chapter fits the facts of experience more simply than does the one that relates all behavior to drives. It suggests that when a man desires something, a norm is established in his brain, we do not know how, and a regulatory process set in motion that tends to make his physical or mental acts conform to it and thus *draws him toward* the object of his desire. Both interpretations of motivation involve complex problems of psychology. The concept of "drive" is more in harmony with a materialistic philosophy since it resembles our ideas of what makes a machine run; that of "draw" is less easy to express, though a study of feedback mechanisms is throwing light on the regulatory aspects of behavior. The difference between the two theories is much sharper in terms of what man actually *feels*. The fact that he wants something is a mental act, and therefore has no scientific standing as a cause of bodily behavior; but his constant sense of wanting, desiring, needing or craving something is

so powerful that he can hardly help regarding it as meaningful. He does not feel as though he were being driven
toward what he wants. In interpreting human motives, the
concept of "draw" is a vital one, though because of the
difficulty of interpreting it in physiological terms it tends
to be underemphasized.

The choice of what we do is made, in most cases, not
because it is right, or will be best for us in the end, or is
the intelligent thing to do, but simply because we *want* to
do it. We like to think that since we are blessed with the
faculty of reason, our acts must always have a rational
basis or be the result of careful thought. As a matter of
fact, most of them come, almost spontaneously, from our
wishes and desires, born in the thalamus and not in the
cerebrum. We are usually *drawn* toward action, not *pushed*
into it. This may be naïve, in terms of modern psychology,
but it seems to fit the facts of experience better than a
complex series of tension reductions. It is in harmony, too,
with man's close involvement with the future, with something *toward which* he always seems to be moving (see
page 239).

The goals which draw us are numberless. Almost from
his birth a man is surrounded by things he wants (or does
not want) and much of his life is spent in choosing which
of these he should pursue or avoid. The great hazard of
his life is the temptation to follow goals that provide immediate satisfaction but prove harmful in the end; and
hence arises the moral dilemma in which he so often finds
himself. Many of his goals are merely temporary, but it is
significant that the most important ones last much longer.
Indeed, the persistence of the self (see Chapter V) with

its specific characteristics is simply the persistence of certain goals throughout life, in large measure unaltered by circumstance. This suggests that in the brain there is much more than a shifting succession of temporary reflex acts. There seems to be here a basic pattern, slowly changing as the individual develops, but maintaining an individuality of its own.

The difference between the concept of "drive" and "draw" is shown even in their terminology. The acts of an animal, and the short-range ones of a man, we call behavior. For the more persistent and significant kinds of human behavior a different word is used, *conduct,* the derivation of which implies the process of being drawn or led, as to an end. Psychology is concerned chiefly with the behavior of any organism, but human conduct involves behavior of a deeper and more permanent sort.

If we accept the interpretation of human motivation here presented, what contributions does it make to the theme of our discussion? There are at least three, I think.

First, it relieves us of the necessity of believing that we are being pushed around by something quite outside ourselves. The problem of freedom (see page 235) is a very deep one, but man *feels* as though he were pursuing (the word is significant) a course of action rather than being driven into it. This sort of motivation is in harmony with the ideals of freedom and responsibility, both fundamental in a religious view of life.

This idea is of importance, too, in education, for unless in this process high ideals are inculcated, all else means little. Under a teacher's skillful hands the student's tastes and desires can be molded; he can be taught to *seek* what is beautiful and good and true. To teach well is not primarily to impart knowledge but to direct the student toward goals that experience has shown will lead to the good life. Many people lack such goals, and life to them is a drifting, not a seeking.

Most important is the all-pervading sense this concept gives that what we are and do depends on the goals toward which we move, on the ideals set up within us which we strive to reach. Man is continually seeking these goals of his desire. If they are low, his satisfactions and accomplishments will be of little worth; if high, the trajectory of his arrow will be loftier than if he aims at a low mark. This orientation of our lives—what we aim at, what our ideals are—is the most important thing about each one of us. Idealism is the framework on which life is built. That the basis of it goes far back in our biological history, to the very stuff that forms us, proves, I believe, its fundamental character.

If a living being is an organized system that tends to maintain itself as an individual and to move, in its development and behavior, toward ends prefigured in its living stuff, if the human individual, through its existence as an organism, experiences this end-seeking as desire and purpose, and if from thence have come the rest of man's varied psychical activities, these will prove important concepts in building the bridge between the material and the spiritual sides of man's nature. A living thing is composed of matter and powered by energy, but if the organization of this physical system is such as to give birth to those human qualities that we call mind, soul and spirit, to the poet's dream of beauty, the scientist's insight and the seer's vision, a way is open by which communication may be established between the philosophies that are entirely naturalistic and those that see something beyond the world of matter and energy. What we are trying to understand are the possibilities present in the organizing power of life as this is exemplified in life's highest manifestation, man himself.

VII

FROM LIFE TO SPIRIT

How such incompatible things as mind and body can be so closely knit together has been philosophy's perennial despair. The suggestion made here, that they are two sides of the same organizing, goal-seeking process evident in bodily development and behavior, may help make their relation somewhat clearer. The problem is complicated, however, by the fact that the psychical part of man has several different aspects. *Mind* is the intelligent, rational, thinking part of him. His *self* or *soul* is what makes him an individual person. To these are sometimes added the concepts of the *ego,* the *psyche* and others, each stressing a side of his psychical life. Beyond all, however, and more difficult to understand, is that nebulous, elusive thing men call the *spirit.* Philosophy does not quite know what to do with this and has left discussion of it chiefly to poets, mystics and men of faith. Psychology never mentions it. Materialism emphatically denies that it exists; but to many people the human spirit is a very precious thing, a warming of the heart, a stirring in the core of being, the place of man's highest ideals where he makes contact with the Divine. It is something real but at the very edge of mystery, something that can be felt but never understood. What a man thinks of the spirit determines his attitude toward his fellow men, his religion and his very concept of God. It lies at the bottom of the philosophical problems I have been discussing.

The word "spirit" is on many tongues today. We praise the spiritual values of our Judaeo-Christian tradition. We urge our fellows to a deeper spiritual life. We say that man is a spiritual being who must worship God in spirit. But what do we mean by this? How can we describe the spirit? Is it anything, after all, but unintelligible superstition? These are difficult questions but they give opportunity for adventurous thinking if we look at man's spirit in the light of what is known about the nature of life. It is possible, I believe, to bring the concept of the spirit down from the clouds of mysticism and to relate it hopefully to the activities of living things from which man's higher attributes have gradually developed. If we admit that his mind (in the word's familiar sense) has evolved from lower levels in the organic world, why not the part of him we call his spirit, too?

Here we appeal again to that germinative idea that every living thing—and man most of all—is an end-seeker, a desirer with an inner directive quality of its own. In time this quality led to the development of man's rational powers, but the nonrational part of his psychic life was by no means superseded. He still is primarily a feeling, desiring and goal-seeking animal, not a thinking one. Despite his pride of intellect, much of his behavior is unreasoned. He may know what should be done to make life happy and society successful, but many times he does not do it. Something overmasters his intelligence. He tries to follow both his new-found, godlike reason, to which he is not yet quite accustomed, and at the same time to satisfy those deeply seated and instinctive wants and urges of his "natural" self that served so well in his long evolutionary struggle and cannot be forgotten now. Part of what he does results from careful thought but most of it comes from following these desires of his, inborn or the results of environmental conditioning.

Intelligence is a cold-blooded affair, logical and machine-like, but desiring is an *emotional* experience, the process of being moved or stirred. My point is that most behavior is thus basically emotional; often in a very low key, to be sure, but emotional, nevertheless, and quite different in character from rational thought. These half-instinctive desires, whatever their source, pour up into consciousness. Here is the source of man's animal nature, his passions, lusts and greeds, which were bred into his being and served him well in the long climb up the evolutionary ladder but cause many of the evils that now beset him. The remarkable fact, however, and one of much significance for our problems here, is that these seemingly inborn desires are by no means always selfish or malignant. From this same source, and charged with the same emotional appeal, come such qualities as man's delight in beauty, his admiration for courage, his love for his fellows, his moral aspirations and his craving for the truth. Their emergence in human evolution, side by side with his baser and more primitive emotions, emphasizes the complexity of that many-sided species which we are. *These deep-*

seated urgencies and desires, coming to flower as the highest expression of what man is and what he might become, one may rightly call, I think, the human spirit.

To associate man's animal-like qualities with his spiritual ones and to derive this most precious of his attributes from the lusts and cravings of a beast will seem to many little short of sacrilege. Spirit, they say, is a more precious thing than this. The great religions of the world have been built around it. Christianity recognizes it as one of the three persons in the Godhead. Spirit interpreted by religion, it maintains, rather than by physiology and psychology, is what men need today. Man *is* a spirit, and to fit him into a purely material world is as hard as to weigh a symphony on a pair of scales.

An advantage of the concept of the spirit offered here is that it places spirit at the very core of *life,* as a manifestation of the *highest form of goal-seeking.* We should remember the words of Bergson, who urges us "to see the life of the body just where it really is, on the road that leads to the life of the spirit. . . . The great error of the doctrines on the spirit has been the idea that by isolating the spiritual life from all the rest, by suspending it in space as high as possible above the earth, they were placing it beyond attack, as if they were not thereby simply exposing it to be taken as an effect of a mirage!"[1]

Spirit is not marked sharply off from "mind" or "soul" but is simply one major aspect of man's psychic life. In what way these so-called spiritual qualities arose in man

---

[1] Henri Bergson, *Creative Evolution,* trans. by Arthur Mitchell, 1911, p. 268, 269.

is one of the major mysteries about him. However we explain them, their chief significance is that they seem *native* to him, a part of his essential character, and mark him off from other animals. They are not equally developed in all men, and in the early evolutionary history of our species were certainly not as conspicuous as they are today; but whenever life's primitive harshness was softened, they were always ready to appear.

If what is called the human spirit has grown from roots far down among the animal instincts, whence it emerged as a stirring of man's emotional life and a refined and heightened seeking for goals above material ones, we must ask if it is merely a series of emotional states and with no deeper significance than this. Yes, many will say, for what deeper significance *could* these states possess, or any others resulting from the activity of a physical system like the brain? Here is a crucial question in our discussion, for religion looks upon the spirit of man as something deeper than transient experience, something that actually exists and may even provide a means of communion between man and God. If the spirit is not touched with any higher significance than what belongs to a curious psychological phenomenon, it can hardly serve a lofty purpose such as this.

Is there any way, aside from an intuitive experience of it, by which one can learn about the spirit? I think there is, and that we can do this best by finding the goals we try to reach under its direction. Our desires at lower levels are a multitude, for bodily needs and gratification of the senses. Their biological origin is obvious, for they are the ends an animal might seek. A man needs something more. When his stomach is full, the lusts of his flesh satisfied and he has had enough of pleasure, he still craves things a glutted beast would never seek; ends he feels instinctively are higher than physical ones and more worth reaching; qualities like beauty, love and truth. Once he experiences the appeal of things like these, he has by that much come to be a man. Over him they wield a strange authority, and to gain them he will sacrifice material needs and pleasures and may even yield his life.

These aspirations are the movings of his spirit. They are his *values* (see page 118), those things to which, through all his history, he has so powerfully been drawn. They are not a random, scattered lot but relatively few, grouped chiefly under that ancient trilogy of the beautiful, the good, the true. That so many men have sought them, and so eagerly, should make us hopeful for this risen ape who holds them in his heart. There is no obvious reason why so often men surrendered comfort, safety, even life itself to dedicate themselves to some great end. Far oftener, indeed, they have been selfish and unlovely in their lives, exemplifying not these values but the seven deadly sins and worse. Throughout the centuries, however, the men who did seek these high goals were those their fellows most admired, the ones who set the ideals for their time. They yielded to something greater than themselves. They are the true heroes of our race, the men whom in our hearts we most admire. It is significant, I think, that whenever some deed of bravery or unselfishness is wrought, men greet it with acclaim. What hosts of such heroes march before our eyes! The countless martyrs slain for conscience' sake. Those men who fought and died to save their homes

—Horatius at the bridge, Arnold von Winkelried gathering the Austrian spears into his breast. All who gave themselves for others—Father Damien with his lepers on Molokai, Walter Reed offering his life to conquer yellow fever, Albert Schweitzer in his hospital at Lambaréné. Men who followed beauty to the end—Beethoven composing when he could no longer hear and Van Gogh painting after his mind was almost gone. Scott dying in the antarctic snows. Galileo whispering the truth. Artists in cold garrets, explorers who did not return, reformers too early for their day, all followers of some star; a few of them acknowledged heroes of our history but countless thousands more now long forgotten, who obeyed an irresistible imperative and moved toward some great goal.

We have seen how difficult it is to explain man's values as the result of natural selection, though selectionists try to do so. Cultural environment can hardly account for them, either, since most cultures are less the causes of man's values than the means by which these values can be reached. As was said in an earlier chapter, values seem to be the expression of tendencies innate in man as man. They are matters of the human spirit. Whence they came and what they mean are questions, I think, not of a curious quirk in man's psychology but of a deeply seated expression of the goals he tries to reach, *the direction toward which he naturally tends to move.* More than any other traits, physical or mental, they express our underlying similarity, the unity of our species, and in a real sense the brotherhood of man. The pursuit of these high values by men of all the races and living under widely different environments and cultures is strong evidence, I think, that there is such a thing as *human* nature which has certain specific qualities and is not so malleable that it can be beaten into any form dictated by the surroundings in which we live.

I should like to suggest, further, that feelings and sensitivities can perhaps help interpret the universe to us. Philosophers who maintain that only through our rational powers can we find out the truth about the world and man forget the part that spiritual experience has in enlightening men's minds. If we were simply glorified computers, without a quiver of feeling in our hearts, we might indeed be intellectual giants but we would miss a very important segment of reality. If we believe that intellect alone can be depended on to tell the truth, and that these emotions, these yearnings in our hearts, have no real significance, we shall find it impossible, I fear, to build upon such a philosophical foundation a faith that will appeal to all men. To come together we must be *drawn* together toward our highest spiritual goals.

Among the goals man reaches for is beauty. This speaks to something deep inside him. His strong emotional response to it is a conspicuous manifestation of the human spirit. Sometimes we are overwhelmed by beauty, as in listening to noble music, reading poetry, standing in the presence of a great work of art or coming upon a breathtaking vista. Such experiences lift us out of ourselves and for a moment we breathe air more rarefied and see "a light that never was, on sea or land." At times like these the spirit takes command, and regardless of evidence or argument, we *know* we are in the presence of something more than the merely material. No machine could have such a sense of exaltation. This love of the beautiful is one of the hardest facts for a materialistic philosophy to explain.

Some aspects of beauty may be intellectually grasped, others experienced but not expressed. Facts in science can be stated in words to other men so that the same information is available to everyone and through rational processes truth may be sorted out from error. Spiritual facts like the feeling for beauty, on the other hand, *cannot* be communicated so. They are truly ineffable. Things of the spirit can be neither measured nor expressed. Language in the sciences is employed to *describe* what exists. In the arts and other spiritual activities, it cannot do this. One can use it, together with paint and marble and musical sounds, only to *evoke* in someone else, if he can, the same feelings that the writer or artist experiences. This difference between the descriptive and the evocative use of language is important for the problems we are discussing.

Beauty involves not matter but order and pattern. If the pigments and canvas of a painting are completely analyzed, or the marble of a statue weighed, or precise measurements made of the vibrations of a violin as it plays a masterpiece, these quantitative facts, as such, have no share in the messages of beauty they convey to us. It is the relation of these parts, in space and time—the pattern created by the artist or composer—that so moves us. Here are spiritual values born. Random notes or a smattering of pigments are of little meaning, for beauty is orderly, as an organism is. It is not matter to which our spirits respond, but patterns made *in* matter. We should remember, too, that beauty is not everywhere, and that ugliness—disorder, randomness—is just as real. We recognize beauty not alone from the qualities it displays but from the contrast it makes with things that are not beautiful.

Whence our sense of beauty comes and why it so appeals to our spirits are among the mysteries. One clue to its source we may find, perhaps, not from aesthetics or philosophy but from biology itself. We have spoken here of the organizing, pattern-making, creative quality of life; the quality that produces organisms—plants, animals and ourselves. It is a significant fact, I think, that these organic patterns are almost invariably thought beautiful by those who look at them. Flowers are among the loveliest of things. Birds and butterflies and shells have charmed mankind through all the years. Some living things delight us more than others, but in all, save those we have been taught to shudder at, some beauty can be found. An organism is not beautiful by *necessity*. To attract a bee, a flower does not need to be beautiful to *us*. Beauty has no *biological* significance. It seems merely a by-product, but as such it tells us much about life, which decorates a simple process with this overplus of loveliness. Is this meaningless or is it an essential part of life itself? Protoplasm—liquid, formless, flowing—is a remarkable craftsman, for the structures that it builds in and around itself would do credit to the most gifted artist. Surely beauty as such has no survival value. The tendency of living stuff to express itself in what is beautiful to us seems to be a quality inherent in it. If this is true, it is a fact of much significance in any study of life, and particularly of man. That we should so admire this living beauty is not strange, for we are come from the same stock ourselves. It is native to us. Unlike other living things, however, we can appreciate it. We respond to the beauties of inorganic nature, too; to sunsets, mountain scenery, wide landscapes and the sea. Beauty can be discovered almost everywhere. Life not only brings it forth but has produced, in man, a being who, by the sensitivities of his spirit, can himself *create* new and undiscovered forms of it.

This is art's great service to mankind. Just as an organism builds random matter into a living bodily pattern, an artist can take formless canvas, paint and marble, musical sounds and the more subtle symbols of words and build them into patterns that catch up some of nature's beauty and interpret it to our spirits. He uses these things as a means of communicating his vision of beauty when it cannot be grasped by the intellect but must speak to something deeper in us. The artist's task is thus to serve as an intermediary between man and nature by expressing the inborn longing of man's spirit for order and beauty, rooted in the very quality of his life, in terms that bring it into harmony with the wider orderliness and beauty in the universe outside.

When we ask what beauty is, therefore, we must approach it, in part, I think, from this biological point of view. Much of what we regard as beautiful is determined by our conditioning, but if we belong to a single species, it is reasonable to suppose that our *basic* desires, the things we naturally value, should be much the same for all of us. What men call beautiful does vary with race and with geography, but we can learn to appreciate the aesthetic values of every culture. So-called primitive art has found an honored place in our museums. Beauty therefore in a sense *is* absolute, and we may define it as *whatever is in harmony with man's innate aesthetic values.*

The appreciation of beauty with which a man is born is subject to change as his taste for it improves. It can be cultivated, as can any other spiritual quality. Partly this comes from greater knowledge and is the intellectual element in the aesthetic process; but most of it, I think, is the result of longer and more intimate contact with what is beautiful. If one lives with a great painting or listens often to a masterpiece, he continues to find beauties in them that he did not grasp before. Sensitivity to spiritual things grows with long contact with them. Meditation is the common technique for spiritual growth. One gains no greater insight by this means into *scientific* truth. One cannot refine one's knowledge of Boyle's law by contemplation of it— though, of course, new relations between it and other scientific ideas may come to one's mind.

The second group of values, the *moral* ones, are both subjective and objective, and involve ideals of behavior, of relations with other people, and thus goals of conduct. These fall into a wide spectrum, from moral values in the strict sense of the word as they are set forth in codes like the Ten Commandments, to qualities like courage, freedom, justice and mercy. These are not always things that *naturally* attract us, as do aesthetic values. Indeed, it is their opposites that often seem to offer prospects of greater pleasure, safety or success. They introduce a concept lacking in other values, that of obligation, of the *ought*. We live a moral life partly because we like it and are drawn to it for its own sake, partly because we know it will be good for us, but partly because we ought to live thus. This sense of

obligation is a value, but a deeper one than mere liking.
It draws us by an inner monitor—*conscience,* if you will
—that tells us what we ought to do. This monitor is not
infallible but differs to some extent in different people and
under different cultures. Just as we are drawn to beauty,
though not always, since our tastes are not infallible, so we
are drawn to what is right, though not always, since our
consciences are not infallible. There are, in a sense, two
grades of conscience. The simpler one, typical of children
and more primitive adults, results from fear of punishment.
The more mature type involves the concept of obligation
and is an expression of the moral values of a particular
individual, his sense of *ought.*

Rightness is a goal we seek, a true value. We must first
discover it, as we discover beauty, by an inner sensitivity,
but we then must *conform* to it by our behavior, often
against attractions drawing us toward quite a different end.
Ethical principles are notoriously difficult to establish. How
to tell right from wrong, *ought* from *ought not,* has always
been one of the hardest problems that man faces. I know
of no safer guide in these deep waters than man's natural,
spiritual sensitivity to what is right. Many will tell us that
this is a purely superficial thing, merely the product of
conditioning, and that it speaks with no authority whatever.
But man is drawn *naturally* toward other high values, as we
have seen, and I believe that this is an example, and a very
important one, of the same thing. If by this means men can
agree on a general basis for their ethical behavior, this will
make easier the construction of that common philosophical
foundation that we seek.

Important evidence from biology is worth considering

in this regard, I think. When the physiological norm of an organism is disturbed by injury or disease, it produces discomfort or pain. This is a warning that something is wrong with the nicely balanced living system. Pain is valuable to us, for if we did not feel it, we might not act in time against the condition that produces it. Pain is the penalty for doing what is biologically "wrong." At a higher level, the situation is like this but far more complex. We are drawn toward a great variety of behavioral goals. If one is fulfilled, this gives us pleasure, but if not, our suffering is often more acute than physical pain. Many goals are incompatible with others. To gain one may prevent achievement of another that would have given us higher satisfaction in the end, and the result at last is sorrow and remorse. The long experience of the race has shown that to achieve some goals brings misery and not happiness in the end. In the conflict between goals, conscience is the arbiter and helps us choose the one that will be spiritually most satisfying. The moral imperative, the *ought,* is thus related to a spiritual norm within us, and behavior that conforms to this is what yields us the highest satisfaction. We may therefore define what is moral as *that which is in harmony with the innate goals of man's behavior*. This is the foundation of a morality that is absolute in the sense that it does not depend on transient and environmental factors but is anchored in the very stuff of which our spiritual sensitivities are born.

One important point with regard to morality should not be forgotten: unless it has a fervor of emotion, unless it is touched with spiritual warmth, it is nothing but formal rectitude. True morality, like beauty, needs more than intellect. It includes a *feeling* of good will for others that is warmed by an inner fire. Discussing some significant facts in history for which a materialistic theory cannot well account, President Conant says: "These are the unselfish ways in which human beings often act with compassion, love, friendliness, self-sacrifice, the desire to mitigate human suffering. In short, it is the problem of 'good,' not 'evil' that requires some other formulation of human personality than that provided by the usual naturalistic moralist."

The spiritual basis of behavior reaches its climax in the value that underlies all other moral ones—love. This is the universal foundation for man's ideal relations with his fellows, the antithesis of the jungle code to which his life so long conformed. If a man loves his neighbor as himself, he does not need to be admonished to refrain from lying, theft and murder. Love is the deepest of all the emotions, the most intensely spiritual part of man. As St. Paul said long ago, no matter how many other virtues a man may have, without love he is nothing. The final answer to the many ills of society today is not in more effective education, better housing, more equitable distribution of wealth, more successful international organization or a banning of the bomb. These will help mightily, and the contributions that can be made by the trained intelligence of mankind are tremendous. The conclusion, however, that *only* through the uses of the intellect can humanity be rescued from the grave danger in which now it stands leaves out something vital. This precious ingredient is the contribution of the spirit manifest as love. Love is more than mere unselfishness; more, even, than concern for the welfare of our fellows. It goes beyond affection and reaches an inner *sympa-*

thy with someone else, a feeling of unity with him so intimate that one seems to share the very feelings of one's
friend. Love is the most powerful force in human life.
Whence it comes is difficult to discover. Natural selection
may have been concerned with the mutual helpfulness
that holds society together, but love is much more than
this. Throughout history, innumerable men and women
have spent their lives, and often laid them down, in selfless
devotion to the welfare of those who offered nothing in
return, sometimes not even gratitude.

Love has its roots, I think, far down in our relations
with all living things. We abhor cruelty to animals and have
a strong feeling of sympathy for the poor brutes that suffer.
This attitude is not love in the narrow sense, but it is more
convincing, to my mind, of the presence of an innate,
spiritual sensitivity in man's heart than is his affection
simply for his fellows. This reverent concern for *all* life,
associated with such men as Albert Schweitzer, St. Francis
of Assisi and hosts of others, speaks of the deep cosmic
roots from which springs the finest flower, human love.
Until men warm their hearts by it and learn to *love* their
neighbors as well as to work with them in society, our
future still will be uncertain. This is what religion, and
especially Christianity, has been preaching for many centuries, though its message has so often been involved with
other things that it has lost its power. Human brotherhood
must be founded not only on the intellectual agreement we
have here been seeking but on love for others.

There are other values that should be included among
the moral ones. *Courage,* the willingness to stand up reso-
lutely against danger and suffering, combines hope and

faith with bravery of heart. Thousands across the centuries exemplify this value, which is more universally admired, I think, than any other; the ideal of the hero, of what a *man* should be. *Freedom,* for which so many have given their lives, is a high value, forgotten today by some who would sacrifice it for security but nevertheless a rallying cry for millions who know that without it they never can be fully men. *Justice,* goal of the universal sense of fairness all men feel, is one of our highest values, for without it, without the equitable administration of just laws, no satisfying society can ever be established. And there are others: *Mercy,* the eagerness to alleviate misery, the hatred of all cruelty and pain, that seeks to lift the burden of suffering from the lives of men. *Loyalty,* which binds men to their friends and the land in which they live and without which society would soon fall apart. *Peace,* that goal of the good life, valued now more than ever since we know that only by its means can man survive to seek his other goals. And what of *humor,* that precious capacity to deflate pretense, to see the incongruous in the life of man, to reduce our tensions and provide a refreshing and wholesome antidote to folly? Surely this deserves to be called a human value. In his highest development, man comes to value the worth of other men; their dignity, their personality, their welfare and their happiness. This is the essence of all moral values. That he desires these things, and often so intensely, helps interpret him to us.

The summit of man's trinity of values is Truth. Through all his seeking, this is his ultimate goal, and the most difficult to reach. Often he seems to discover truth only to find that it eludes his search. The truth of which one generation is convinced may later be proved false. And yet we feel that truth exists and that we certainly can find out what it is. This is the great conclusion of science—that truth can finally be separated from error. Man is blessed with a strong inborn sense of wanting to find out, perhaps because he comes from simian ancestry! A sense beyond mere curiosity, however, a longing to get at the secrets of the universe, to pierce the veil that in so many places covers the unknown, distinguishes him. He is a born adventurer. The frontiers of geography were the first to tempt him from the safety of his homeland, and until our own century have provided the chief incentive for explorers. The frontiers of the imagination are now vastly wider, and boys who once would have dreamed of discovering the poles are dreaming now of spaceships for a voyage to Mars. The most absorbing of human adventures with the unknown has long been scientific exploration. Beyond this beckons the undiscovered continent of man and the deep problems of philosophy that his life poses. Always the great adventure is the search for truth, wherever it is hidden.

One of the most important questions we can ask is why man is such an insatiable adventurer for truth. What he seeks is not primarily that which will make him richer or society more prosperous but something, instead, that will satisfy this perpetual craving to *find out*. This quest, whatever the cause of it may be, is deeply imbedded in man's nature and is a high value to which he always has been drawn. It is one of his most hopeful qualities and augurs well for what the years may bring him. For the common faith we seek, truth must be the firm foundation. If we are guided by our instinctive love of it and can avoid the perils of ignorance, bigotry and dogmatism, truth, indeed, shall help to make us free.

In the discussion of these values the important point, I think, is that our appreciation for them becomes more acute as it is cultivated. In aesthetics we call this appreciation *taste;* in morals, *conscience,* and in the search for truth, *intuition.* The concept this presents of man is of a living system, not neutral, but delicately sensitive to specific qualities in his environment that may best be called spiritual. This is a very different view from the one held by many, which looks upon him as the product of factors outside himself, possessing no inner character of his own and certainly no spiritual nature, but I believe it is a truer one.

A discussion of the human spirit bears closely on the main question we have been considering—the relation of materialistic to religious philosophies of life. If what is called "spirit" is no more than an aspect of the physical side of man, as are digestion, respiration and his various physical activities, this favors the materialistic argument; but if there is evidence of something in man's nature that has another origin than biochemical and bioelectrical changes in his nervous system, then from this source comes vindication for the man of religious faith. What has been presented here is certainly not conclusive evidence for either side, but it shows that in man, as he attains a high level of development, there is in his thought and in his behavior something very hard to explain in terms of matter and energy alone, something that draws him toward truly spiritual goals. This is emotion, but emotion far above that which animals feel, where it is usually grounded in the physiological processes that accompany hunger, lust or combat, and which have been important in the selective struggle. The quieter emotions, directed toward the realization of such values as beauty, goodness, love and truth, are much more difficult to explain. Not until man emerged from brutishness did he actively seek goals like these. It is in his spirit and not only in his intellect that he is unique in the living world. These essentially spiritual values, I believe, are the characteristic qualities of man, the highest expression of his goal-seeking. The remarkable fact about them, pointed out on an earlier page, is that the most significant ones are characteristic of all normal human beings.

Whatever spirit actually is, its origin confronts materialism with a serious dilemma. No philosophy, I am sure, that leaves it out will ever satisfy mankind. One has to admit either that this ethereal quality is a "natural" product, in which case he must recognize in the material world possibilities quite unsuspected and unexplained, or he must concede that there *is* such an immaterial thing as spirit in the universe and that in some way it is associated with life.

The presence in man of his two contrasting attributes— intellect and spirit—is of the utmost significance in the problems we have been discussing. Intellect, a relatively recent offshoot from the ancient instinctive stock, is cool, exact, logical, quantitative, tough-minded, hardheaded. It delights in science and its methods, and sees in natural processes the solid basis for a philosophy that tends to be materialistic. Spirit, on the other hand, the primitive side of man, is closer to life itself. In its warmth of emotion and its vivid feelings it is more in harmony with the claims of faith. Religion is the place where these two meet. Man is a thinker but he is a poet, too, and both activities are essential for his life. The beginnings of the contrast between the two philosophies we are discussing go far back in human evolution. They are expressions of the difference between these two aspects of his psychic life. I hope it will be possible to reconcile this difference between mind and spirit by discovering in the life of the organism itself, as in these pages we are trying to do, a bridge that will bring them more intimately together.

VIII

FROM LIFE TO GOD

T HE ATTEMPT TO discover in the fact of
biological organization a possible basis for understanding
the relationship between mind and body will be looked on
with some sympathy, I hope, if only because no more
reasonable suggestion is at hand. To carry this idea still
further and try to find in the development of the living
organism the process that gives birth to "soul" and to
"spirit" will seem to many little more than a fantastic spec-
ulation. The materialist scoffs at such an idea, and to the
man of faith it appears a feeble substitute indeed for the
sublime origin to which he attributes these most precious
of his convictions.

The great issue between the two philosophies, however,
goes much deeper. Some may be willing to grant that in
mankind there is a faculty called "spirit," an exquisite
sensitivity to beauty and goodness worthy of our admiration and even of our reverence, and that around this can
be built a faith in man that ministers, at least to humanists,
as a religion. This is as far as a naturalistic philosopher will
go. Religion does not stop here but makes the adventurous

leap from the spirit of man to a Universal Spirit it calls God. The power of religion lies in the belief that God is indeed the final reality in the universe; but for an unbeliever this idea is so preposterous, so impossible in an enlightened age, that he never really takes it seriously. Between the two philosophies here is the final issue joined.

The suggestion that evidence from biology might be pursued far enough to become involved in this great confrontation will doubtless seem absurd to many people. The laboratory is not the place where most would expect to discover God, and in fact more men have lost their faith there than have found it. Let us not falter now, however, in the endeavor undertaken at the beginning of these discussions—to bring the philosophies of materialism and religion closer to each other by building a bridge between them that is based on the great fact of *life*. We met life first in simple material systems and have followed it through successively higher manifestations in the life of man. The phenomena of organization, regulatory behavior and goal-seeking have so far proved fruitful enough, I think, to encourage an attempt to throw this final span of the bridge out into the unknown; to discover whether across it a contact may be made with something far greater than we have yet encountered. Perhaps there is no place to anchor it at all and the whole structure may have to be abandoned, leaving as the only basis for a sound philosophy the solid rock of matter to which it first was fastened. I, for one, am willing to take the risk of trying to find out; and risk it is, for a biologist who strays far enough from the orthodoxies of his profession to discuss seriously any

bearing of it on the possibility of God's existence may
lose both the attention and the respect of his associates.
Denial of God has been so long a basis for the confident
dogmatism of unbelievers and for their castigation of all
religion as superstition and unsubstantiated mysticism that
any serious change on the part of most of them is now
improbable.

If God exists, He must be far more vast and incomprehensible than men used to think Him. Theologians have
often sought to contain Him in their words, to no avail.
The official belief of the Church of Rome, based on the
teachings of St. Thomas Aquinas, is that God's existence
can surely be known by the natural light of human reason
as it studies the physical universe. The proofs proposed,
drawn from ideas of motion, cosmology, contingency,   ·
transcendency and teleology, are clothed in profound
words, but though they may carry certainty to Thomists, I
am afraid they leave most others unconvinced. Philosophers, with all their skill in dialectic, have not been able to
satisfy many that God is, or shown how we can know Him.
Some see God immanent in the whole creation, interfusing
it throughout, but others think of Him as "utterly other,"
quite outside the realm of space and time. Tillich even
believes in a "God above God."

Throughout history, faith in God has been nourished
less by rational argument than by an inner *conviction* that
God exists. In earlier days, however, conclusions of the
so-called natural theology, based on evidence from science,
were widely accepted by those who saw "the presence and
wisdom of God as manifested in the Natural and Moral

World."[1] Arguments from this source have less influence today, since many facts formerly attributed to divine causation have come to be explained in other ways. It would be unwise, however, to repudiate *all* rational evidence that there is a God simply because much of it in the past was unconvincing, for there are many facts in harmony with the idea that God exists, although they furnish no sure proof for this conclusion. To base all belief in God on divine revelation or on spiritual experience and to disregard the vast body of human knowledge would not be worthy of man's abilities or of the profound problem with which he here is dealing. The arguments of the world's great thinkers on this matter are far beyond the limitations of the present volume, but there are three general facts about the universe that are of importance in relation to our discussion which should be mentioned here. They concern the ideas of Order, Creativeness and Aspiration.

Order

Science depends for its very existence on the orderliness and dependability of the universe. Nature today will give to any question the same answer that she did yesterday and will again tomorrow. This constancy can often be reduced to simple, quantitative facts that have acquired the very name of *constants*—the speed of light, the gravitational constant, Planck's constant and many others—which seem to be built into the heart of things. This concept of the uniformity of nature is the chief contribution of science

---

[1] From the wording of the deed of gift establishing the Silliman Memorial Lectures at Yale University.

to philosophy, but it is still an assumption, still an article of faith. For all we know, there may be a subtle sort of chaos in the universe, and the laws of nature may be superficial things that sometimes may be broken. Both science and religion share a faith in the dependability of the universe, though expressing it in different ways. It is the chief bond between them. If God exists, He must be a God on whom we can depend.

Among living things, order shows itself in a precise relationship between the different parts of a system, in space and time; in short, in a pattern. Uniformity (homogeneity or randomness) is *absence* of order. In an organism, order develops from such randomness. On an earlier page I showed that food, largely in a disorganized condition, is taken into the digestive system of an animal and further broken down until its molecules are in a soluble and almost completely random state. They are then absorbed, and finally are built into the system of the body as part of an orderly organic pattern. Life is a process that continually imposes order on randomness in this fashion; and organic *form,* a quality characteristic of living things, is one of its products. The increasing complexity of this biological order is evident both in the development of an individual from egg to maturity and in the process of evolution from primitive creatures up to man.

Such order is particularly impressive because of the fact that, in reaching it, life moves in a direction opposite to the one taken by lifeless matter. In the latter, there is progressively more *dis*order, randomness, or what the physicist calls entropy. The essence of the second law of thermodynamics is that entropy tends continually to in-

crease and energy to become evenly distributed so that
the system as a consequence will in time "run down" and
become uniform throughout. One can see how this is so,
for particles of matter when free to move are in continual
agitation, colliding and pushing each other about until
whatever different types of particles there are become
evenly distributed, like the contents of a cement mixer. As
one distinguished physicist has put it, the natural tendency
of things is to approach the chaotic state unless something
is done to prevent it. But in a living organism it *is* prevented. Here occurs a result akin to the sorting out of
elements in a mixture. This is what takes place when food
is built into the patterned system of the body and when
sponge cells (see page 101), shaken apart, draw themselves together to form a sponge again. In lifelessness there
is a mixing process that leads to disorder, but in life, a
sorting one that makes for order. This is the basic difference between living and lifeless matter.

The most notable example of order in the living world
is the organism. Here is not simple orderliness but a complex, three-dimensional system, its different parts closely
related in structure and activity and united into a single
whole. The organism holds the secret of life, and in no small
measure, I believe, the secret of man. All our knowledge
of the chemistry of protoplasm and its genes has told us
little about the organism of which they are parts. Something
seems to be involved here unlike the more familiar processes of nature. I have elsewhere called it the Principle of
Organization, and even suggested that it may be one of
the attributes of Deity.

There is order in the lifeless world, too, notably in

crystals, but this is a different sort of order, rigid and un-changing, built by the addition of molecules upon the sur-face. In a living thing, on the contrary, matter continually enters and departs, organic form being preserved in a dy-namic equilibrium, a "steady state." An organism is essen-tially a semifluid system, a mass of protoplasm with firmer material secreted in and around it. To produce and main-tain order in such a system is a very different problem from the methodical piling up of molecules that makes a crystal.

A continual encounter seems therefore to be taking place between the forces manifest in lifeless matter, which tend toward randomness and uniformity, and those of life, which fashion matter into the orderly and almost infinitely various forms of living organisms. Order in a living thing results from inner molding, not outer accretion. The great enigma is how life accomplishes this task. Living stuff in contact with dead matter exerts an influence on it, drawing it in, shaping it and creating out of it a pattern so specific and so constant that it can be used to identify a plant or animal. This power does not arise spontaneously in lifeless matter —at least we have not yet observed it—but is passed on in a sort of apostolic succession from one living cell to those that are descended from it. Biologists are beginning to learn the language, so to speak—the code, the script— by which the traits of an organism are catalogued in its genes, but this does not tell how a molecule of DNA molds formless matter into a three-dimensional living thing. Something formative there must be in protoplasm that im-poses this complex order on dead stuff.

The orderliness of the universe powerfully appeals to those who see in it the sort of intelligible plan which Paley

pointed to as proof that life was the work of a great De-
signer. We know now that the beautiful adaptations which
so persuaded him have come about through the action of
natural selection. But there may be a deeper order in the
universe than these organic patterns. Says Einstein: "A
conviction, akin to religious feeling, of the rationality or
intelligibility of the world lies behind all scientific work of
a high order. This firm belief, a belief bound up with deep
feeling, in a superior mind that reveals itself in the world
of experience, represents my conception of God."[2] Though
this immanence of order in things gives no certainty that
God exists, it brings conviction to many people that behind
outward phenomena there *is* a supreme intelligence. In
these days when so much is attributed to chance and accident, it is reassuring, I think, to find that at the heart of
nature something does make for order; something that
pushes up against the downward thrust of randomness and
chance and, in a world that long was without form and
void, moves toward a cosmos. "Order is heaven's first law,"
and in this universal orderliness that inheres in matter and
energy there is something that may be a manifestation of
the Divine.

Creativeness

Perhaps the most significant fact about the universe is
that it exists at all. How it came into being has never ceased
to puzzle men, and the answer is not yet. Cosmogonists
are still by no means sure of just what happened. Some

---

[2] Albert Einstein, "The Faith of Great Scientists," *The American
Weekly,* 1948.

believe it all began a few billion years ago with a tremendous explosion which, in brief space and time, formed
all the elements and sent matter hurtling outward into
space. Another school has proposed the startling theory
that matter is continually being created, fed into the stock
already in the universe and in time pulled together to make
fresh galaxies and newborn worlds. Neither hypothesis
gives the final answer, and perhaps this never *can* be found.
Infinity and eternity are words loosely used in such discussions, but to our minds they still are almost meaningless.
From earliest times, most men have believed that creation
is the work of a being they call God. It is as Creator that
God is first described in the Bible; not as the God of
righteousness or wisdom or justice or love, but as the
Maker of heaven and earth at the completion of whose
great task "the morning stars sang together."

The universe is unspeakably vast, both as to space and
time. Its age (if it be not ageless) is reckoned in billions
of years; its extent (if it be not infinite) in billions of
light years, each light year seven thousand billion miles; its
galaxies numbered in the billions and with billions of stars
in each. All this is so far beyond our powers of comprehension that the intellect balks at even trying to make sense
of it. To many, it is inconceivable that such a system could
have come into being by itself. Even the Deists admit that
God created the universe in the beginning, though He has
let it run by itself since then. One of the remarkable things
about it is that it does not "run down," as the Second
Law suggests it should. What, we may ask, "wound it up"
in the first place, and why is not maximum entropy the end
of the process, and a completely homogeneous and quiet

state? This seems unlikely, for the universe continually changes, and the galaxies are rushing away from one another toward outer space. Our own Milky Way spins like a giant pinwheel. These changes are beginning to be described in scientific terms, and some of them to be understood. Our knowledge of cosmogony today makes it no longer true, some people say, that the heavens declare the glory of God. Nevertheless, the power that brought this mighty system into being is still worthy of our reverence, whatever philosophical position we may hold.

Such cosmic restlessness is not creation, however, for creation means the appearance of something *new*. This involves a basic question. We are accustomed to speak of the creation of the world, or of the origin of life, or of the creativity of an artist. Are these real *novelties,* we ask, and thus true creations? Our answer commits us to a determined or an undetermined universe, to one mechanically bound or one that is free. If what happens in the universe is all determined in advance, and "the first morning of creation wrote what the last day of reckoning shall read," then there is never *anything* new, no creation, no innovation, but simply the endless unrolling and effectuation of what had already been decided in the womb of time. Perhaps we have been wrong in assuming that real creation has occurred. Perhaps the Preacher was on firmer ground when he said, "There is no new thing under the sun." Ideas about determinism today have changed considerably from what they once were, however, and most philosophers would now admit the possibility of novelty, and thus of creativeness. Let us hope that they are right, for a universe without the opportunity for change, without the excitement of the unexpected, without the joy of creativity, would be a sorry universe indeed. At least in the beginning new things were born, and this seems to have been happening ever since.

It is the lifeless portion of the universe that is relatively changeless. Since the beginning of time it has continued to produce the same sorts of things—electrons, protons, atoms, molecules, planets, stars and galaxies. Only when matter became endowed with life did something really new begin to happen. After the simpler molecules of inorganic substances had combined into larger and more complex ones, these underwent a profound change and in some way became alive. Then creation began to accelerate. With life there came the exuberant variety of forms that now delight our eyes and warm our hearts. Through the agency of natural selection, changes were channeled in various directions, and the long pageant of organic evolution began to move. This resulted in the successive production of new species of animals and plants, millions of them, and in their successive extinction, but it has taken more than two billion years to bring forth the living things that we know now. The highest product of evolution, man himself, has vastly speeded up the creative process. Creation on earth now centers primarily in him. He is endowed with imagination, the necessary basis for creativity, since by its means those most precious products of the mind, new ideas, come into being. In a burst of speed in the last few thousand years, accelerating from century to century and reaching a high point today, human creativity has exceeded anything ever dreamed of in the past.

If "the old order changeth, giving place to new," and

in the history of organisms and of man new things do come out from old, what bearing, we may ask, does all this have on the question as to whether God exists? The agnostic says at once it has *no* bearing. You need no creator to explain change and novelty, for these things happen by natural law. They are like an elaborate pattern in a display of fireworks that is simply the realization, against the night sky, of a series of changes prefigured in the structure of the piece and taking place inevitably, once the match has been applied. So is it with evolutionary creativeness. This is far more complex than fireworks but the same cause-and-effect necessity is there. Naturally, there will in time be changes and apparent novelties. The same is true, the agnostic says, of the chain of causes that leads to new ideas in the brain of man.

But the remarkable fact about creativity where we see it at its highest—in the traits we value most in man—is that it has brought forth qualities like love of beauty and love of one's fellows that are very hard to account for by the selection of random changes or any mechanical process. If natural selection cannot explain these, there would seem to be in the creative process itself, or in man, a tendency toward their production. The flights of inspiration by poet, artist, scientist and saint are hard to interpret as the creations of protoplasmic chemistry or of a "fortuitous concourse of atoms." Can these factors account for Shakespeare, or Darwin, or Einstein, or Toscanini? Or did these men (and do all men on a lesser scale) possess within themselves a bit of the generative force that orients human beings toward high goals? How, in the strange species which is ours, did there come to birth those traits that we call spiritual? Man is surely the product of a creative process more wonderful than that which has made the immense but lifeless cosmos where he dwells. The concept of Creativeness is an expression, in rational terms, of the inner certainty felt by many that the universe, almost infinite in its extent but fashioned with exquisite delicacy in its most minute parts, could never be the result of chance or of impersonal necessity but must be the work of a Creator. This conviction carries no proof, but it is the oldest expression in man's heart of what God really is.

Aspiration

Order and creativeness, qualities inherent in all life, are important ideas, but in the momentous question we are here considering they do little more than suggest that in nature there is something that points to the Divine. This may help to reassure those who have been convinced on other grounds already, but will hardly persuade a tough-minded naturalistic philosopher that there is a God. Such belief more often comes through an inner sense or feeling of God's existence that transcends rational evidence. The question we now must ask is whether a knowledge of life, and particularly of the phenomenon of organization and goal-seeking, which we have found fruitful in other problems, can offer any support to this conviction that in the universe there is a God.

We have seen how sensitive man is to certain high values. This was not always so. The values sought by primitive man were material and earthy ones—the satisfaction of needs for food, sex and safety. As he progressed, these goals, indeed, remained but from them grew a craving

for much higher ones like beauty, goodness and truth. His
evolution as man followed the elevation of his goals from
appetites to aspirations. Why he was drawn upward thus
cannot easily be explained by a process of selection. In his
earlier days, when brutal and selfish patterns of behavior
were necessary for survival, he had little opportunity to
seek these higher values, for he was distracted by more
immediate and pressing matters that crowded out such
things, just as noise prevents our listening to distant music.
In the valley far below a certain hillside farm that I know
well there rushes a mountain stream. One cannot hear it
in the daytime but on quiet evenings, when other sounds
are hushed, the far-off roar of hurrying water becomes
audible. In some such way as this, I think, man's true
nature begins to emerge whenever selfish desires and the
distractions of circumstance become less powerful. It is
significant that these emerging traits so rarely lead to
viciousness, to a devotion to lust and greed and merely
sensual and selfish gratification. It is true that many men,
and brilliant ones, are little better than the beasts, but the
remarkable fact remains that as man has become more and
more the master of his destiny, he has tended oftener to
display those qualities that we call spiritual. His life is less
often an orgy than an aspiration.

The problem remains as to why this latent seeking after
high values came to be present in man's nature. A consideration of it, I believe, will bear closely on our present topic,
but before it can be discussed fully, I shall have to turn
again to evidence from biology.

Culture is the great body of knowledge, experience and
behavior that man has developed since the close of his

purely biological evolution, and has transmitted by imitation and education from one generation to the next. Before cultural evolution began, natural selection had provided our human stock with the *capacity* for culture. For a long time this was not exercised, since learning is a slow process. The ability was there before it was fully employed. Alfred Russel Wallace, Darwin's great contemporary, through long and close association with very primitive East Indian savages, found that they had great native abilities; as great, he suggested, as those of highly civilized contemporary Europeans. He did not see how natural selection could have provided this ability, since it was far beyond the necessity of the people who possessed it, and he carried on a famous polemic with Darwin on the problem. Darwin's reply, in essence, was that these natives, although primitive by our standards, really did need to exercise a great amount of thought and mental ability to live successfully. Today we would be more likely to say that by the time these primitive savages had become human they had acquired, through selection, the ability, in body and mind, to develop culture. This ability could be used, when men learned enough, to carry on a complex culture as well as a simple one. This is proved today by the ability of many members of so-called primitive races to acquire a high degree of education and intellectual development. What natural selection produced, so runs the argument, was not a series of specific cultural abilities—to build machines, or gain aesthetic skills, or do research in mathematics—but rather the general *capacity* to do these things. Some evolutionists are inclined today to look on this capacity as a sort of package of abilities; most, on balance, being serviceable to man and thus tending toward his survival (or else natural selection could not have been effective) but some being harmful. This does not seem to me to solve the problem of the widespread presence of certain values in man, unless we assume, for example, that love for beauty just happened to be caught up with various other things when human culture evolved. To be sure, by no means *all* men pursue these high values of which we have been speaking, but the remarkable thing is that most of them accept such goals as worthy to be sought.

I should like to make here another unorthodox suggestion. Man's value-seeking traits doubtless have a genetic basis, and it is well understood that what a gene or a given genetic constitution determines is not a specific *trait* but a specific *reaction* to a specific environment. Whether one "burns" or "tans," for example, when exposed to bright sunlight is determined by the inherited reaction of his skin to light. In their ancestry, most organisms have been exposed to a very wide range of environmental factors. It is now possible, however, to expand this range considerably by using chemical substances or physical factors that have never existed on earth before but have been produced by modern technology. The results cannot be predicted. What the reaction of an organism will be to these factors obviously does not depend on selection undergone by his ancestors but on a genetic constitution developed by other means. Over a long period of time, therefore, this constitution may be the result of a sort of "crypto-evolution" the effects of which will not be manifest until the particular environment appears that is necessary to bring these qualities to expression. The onset of cultural evolution produced a radical environmental change of this sort. It is reasonable to believe, therefore, that this would have favored the emergence of traits the potentialities for which had long existed but would not have been suspected. To this class of traits might belong man's pursuit of high values when favorable conditions once appeared as the result of an advancing civilization. Why these emerging qualities should be those leading to admiration of beauty, goodness and truth instead of ugliness, evil and falsehood is not clear unless (as I shall soon propose) the former values are in harmony with the ultimate character of the universe itself.

All this leads to the conclusion, astonishing enough to most students of evolution and of man, that in his inmost heart he is disposed to be a lover of the beautiful and of his fellows, and moves toward a continually greater sensitivity to high values; not as a result of the selective process alone, or only from the environment in which he dwells, but from tendencies inherent in his very nature (see page 174). This suggestion is so radical, both for psychology and biology, that I can hear the chorus of dissent that will arise at once against it. The idea runs head-on into two firmly entrenched but opposing orthodoxies.

The first of these is biological and maintains that evolutionary change is unguided, that it does not take place in any particular direction; in other words, that there is no evidence of *orthogenesis,* a very bad word among selectionists. That men tend naturally to be seekers after beauty and righteousness is as preposterous, say many, as that they naturally tend to be brown-eyed. One may reply that the objection to orthogenesis has come from a study of *biological* evolution, which results from the natural selection of random genetic changes. Most of the qualities of man which we have just been describing, however, have arisen during the period of his *cultural* evolution, when natural selection has played a negligible part. These qualities are not inherited, differential reproduction has had no share in their development, and the time during which they have appeared was far too short for selection in the Darwinian sense to be an important factor. As has previously been shown (see page 122), there is a certain selectiveness among them, just as there is in the competition between diverse political systems, business practices, teaching methods and the techniques which change as civilization progresses. This "cultural orthogenesis" is the directiveness given to these tendencies by human beings *themselves*. Conditions today are far more favorable than before for the emergence of many specific innate but latent qualities that would never have had a chance to appear until a civilized culture was achieved. My idea is that these changed conditions do not themselves cause the changes that appear but simply that they make possible the expression of these changes, somewhat as developer brings out the picture on an exposed photographic film.

The suggestion that men are basically good violates an orthodoxy of quite a different sort, the doctrine of "original sin." This maintains that man is not inherently aspiring but inherently *wicked* and must therefore be saved, or regenerated, or at least changed completely from his natural self. Those who support this idea will find it impossible to admit that in a creature whom they regard as basically wicked there is a core of "original goodness." Believers in human depravity are not as numerous now as

they were in Calvin's day, but the suggestion made here
will be opposed by those who doubt, for other reasons,
that man *is* naturally good. They will ask the pertinent
question as to why, if man is intrinsically so superior, the
world over which he presides is in such a sorry state
today. The present widespread vulgarity of taste in almost
every field would hardly be tolerated, he says, by a people
who instinctively love beauty. The rapidly rising tide of
crime, and the shocking state of morality, both private and
public, do not suggest that men today are natural lovers
of righteousness; and in the shadow of Hiroshima and
Auschwitz it seems preposterous to maintain that they are
really lovers of their fellows.

The answers to these serious objections lie not so much
in the theoretical basis of the suggestion I have made as in
the actual historical record. I do not maintain that man
now always loves beauty and practices altruism, or moves
toward the truth, but that if his inner nature has a chance
to express itself, it will show that he is moving *toward*
those ends, stumblingly and slow, but moving. We must
now inquire whether this actually is true. What does the
record say? What we find will be of much importance for
the argument I am presenting.

It is hard to measure progress in aesthetics, for no good
yardstick for the purpose is available. There certainly has
been no cumulative advance here such as the sciences have
shown, particularly in recent centuries. Men sought for
beauty even at the dawn of history, and have created it at
many times and places ever since. Popular appreciation of
it has risen and fallen, but today many more millions than
ever in the world before are concerned with beauty in its

varied forms—with music and poetry, with drama, and painting, and sculpture and architecture; not concerned in a professional sense, most of them, but as amateurs in the true meaning of the word, as *lovers* of beauty and the arts. Their taste is often not the best and their efforts may be crude, but they are sincere. The millions of "Sunday painters," and the innumerable amateur orchestras and dramatic groups present a really moving picture of man's eager search for aesthetic satisfaction. Never before have there been so many intelligent attempts to make our towns and cities more attractive places in which to live. Fine old houses that not long ago would have been pulled down if they interfered with "progress" are preserved today. Billboards are disappearing. Attractive vistas, threatened by commercialism, find many defenders. We do not tolerate ugliness so readily as we used to, nor connive so often at the destruction of beauty anywhere. There is vast room for improvement, certainly, but we are on the move, and in the right direction. Something in man that has been emerging with the years becomes an ever more important part of what he does. In America this change has recently been taking place so fast that some have called it a cultural explosion. The arts are no longer a prerogative of the few, as they used to be, but are coming to be recognized as everybody's birthright. Even government is showing interest in their encouragement. Selective survival cannot account for this upsurge of aesthetics, nor can cultural conditions, for men are not being modified by their culture pattern as much as they themselves are modifying *it*. Why should men seek beauty so eagerly, and with such unanimity? Is it not reasonable to conclude that *by their very nature* they are lovers of it?

But is man becoming more and more a lover of his fellows? This is not easy to prove, but I believe a case can be made out for it. One starts here with a handicap, of course, for in man's evolutionary history a premium was put at first on selfishness, not selflessness. Even after what we call civilization began, cruelty, torture and inhuman behavior were commonplace. In pagan cultures the most hideous brutalities were practiced. Not until Christianity became widespread was much thought given to the loving of one's neighbor; but even the history of the church itself has been smirched by unspeakable atrocities. The tortures of the Inquisition will never be forgotten, nor that Calvin burned Servetus at the stake.

But a gentler spirit has come over man in recent times. Think, for example, of how our attitude toward animals has changed. Through the ages they were subjected to the most brutal treatment—sometimes thoughtless, often intentional and for human entertainment. From the spectacular cruelties of Nero's day to the cock-fighting and bear-baiting of more recent times, man's concern for the suffering of animals was slight. After all, they surely had no souls! Were they not created for man's service and pleasure? Why worry if a horse was beaten to death trying to draw too heavy a load? But such acts offend something deep in the human heart; a feeling of sympathy for the poor beasts that suffer; an identification, to some degree, of our own selves with them. In the upsurge of reform that marked the nineteenth century, societies for the prevention of cruelty to animals began to be established. Their work, and their attitude toward the brute creation, are now strongly supported in all civilized lands. Indeed, care for the comfort and welfare of animals is now one of the marks by which the level of a civilization can be judged.

He would be a misanthrope indeed who did not also see, in the past century or two, I think, the beginning of a more benign attitude of man toward man. In enlightened nations, human beings are no longer kept in slavery. Criminals and the insane have better treatment. Helpless children have been freed from cruelty and hardship, so far as the law can do it. It is a hopeful fact that barbarous acts are called *inhuman*—not those to be expected of a man. The very word "humanity" has come to be synonymous with compassion. That cruelty and hatred still are rampant, no one who remembers the savagery of war and genocide or who watches racial enmity today can deny; but dark as the picture is, it has been growing brighter. Great programs for medical care, relief of suffering and the amelioration of men's lives have been established, not only in our own nation but for the relief of need wherever it occurs. Never before has so much thought and effort— and money—been bestowed on the care of the sick, the aged, the infirm and the poor as there is today. Did this happen in the great Enlightenment of the eighteenth century, with all its progress? Did the enormous material advances of the nineteenth do more than begin some of these reforms. Not until our own century has accomplishment in this direction been so great. In civilized societies we no longer let men starve to death, or perish in the gutter, if we can help it. In many ways we actually come closer to practicing the Golden Rule today, on a nationwide or even a worldwide scale, than men have ever done before. Some of this advance has doubtless been the result of enlightened self-interest and the uses of intelligence to help usher in the millennium by economics; but although such factors have been concerned in all man's progress and must certainly be emphasized to the utmost if this is to continue, we should remember that there are here involved, to a major degree, those attributes of man that are not merely intellectual but are emotional and spiritual.

Such, briefly, is the case for the thesis that man naturally seeks for beauty and tries to create it, and more today than ever before; and that his concern for the welfare of his fellows has progressively increased. To the many who deny that man has made real progress, and those who see vast ugliness and hatred everywhere, the picture drawn here is a caricature. A world stumbling to its doom is not a place where love and beauty dwell. But let us not be concerned so much with what man is today as with the progress he has made and the direction in which he is moving now. Historians, comparing the present with the past, have good reason, I believe, to be encouraged.

But what shall we say of man's search for his crowning value, Truth? Surely there is a vast deal of ignorance, superstition, prejudice and sheer intellectual perversity in the world. Men still cling to ancient beliefs, long proved to be erroneous, and often seem more eager to uphold an opinion because of its wide acceptance than because it actually is true. In one field of human activity, however— the sciences—truth is certainly being sought more persistently and by more people than ever in the past. Through their understanding of science, elementary as this often is, men are coming to see how by this means one can discover what truth is and how it may be separated from error. This wholesome lesson is being carried over, I believe, into philosophy, religion and other areas where truth is more difficult to come by. The devoted search for it in science also has the happy effect not only of reducing ignorance but of bringing men together in friendly participation in a common cause that transcends national, racial and religious barriers. The international community of scientists is in many ways a model for the greater community of man that we all hope will come. There has been search for scientific truth for centuries, but only in recent years, when the number of people who can appreciate it has greatly increased, has science assumed a major role in our society.

But let us return to the main argument of the present chapter, an examination of evidence for the existence of a God. If the universe is fundamentally a random one, guided by forces impersonal and purposeless, human behavior should show no tendency to move in particular directions. That in man, the most complex product of the evolutionary process, behavior *does* show such tendencies is of much significance. Why *should* men aspire so generally to beauty and selflessness and truth? One would not expect this of a biochemical mechanism. The orderly pattern beauty shows should have no attraction, one would think, for a creature whose very history is directionless; and if survival is the only key to progress, a man who gives his life to save his friend is not commendable but merely foolish. If the observer from another planet whom we have imagined as a visitor to Earth in the Pleistocene had watched the first steps in the evolution of our species, and if he had been sufficiently perspicacious, he might have predicted the triumphs of intelligence and ingenuity to be shown in time by what was to become *Homo sapiens,* but I much doubt if he would have guessed that among the descendants of those chattering and flea-bitten ape-men there would someday appear artists and poets and seers, humanitarians and saints. The things that spiritually-minded men like these are doing now seem quite out of harmony with the behavior of descendants of such an ancestor, however intelligent. To be sure, many who call themselves materialists today are sincere lovers of beauty, of their fellows and of truth; but they are so, I think, in spite of and not because of their philosophy. They are humane. They share with all mankind the great endowment that makes them *men.*

What *is* it that draws us so powerfully toward those high goals that are the marks of man? The only satisfying answer to me is that in the universe there is something of which beauty and love and truth and the human spirit all are parts; something infinite in time and space, the highest of goals, to which man's life, though often unconsciously, is ever seeking to conform. This is the climax of the process of goal-seeking which we have seen expressed in all life, from bodily development to man's loftiest spiritual attributes. Man is a seeker, and God his highest goal. Call this goal whatever name we will, when life is freed from the shackles that circumstance puts on it, this is what life seeks; not by a random and unguided course but through an inner directiveness or sensitivity like that by which the needle seeks the pole, or a radio picks up a broadcast. Gardner Murphy has expressed this well: "The living

organism is a sort of 'harmonic,' a reduplication of, a reso-
nance with, vaster forces which he can perhaps only hope
to know as he sees his own nature expressed more grandly
in space-time terms. . . . The microcosm which is man . . .
is perhaps capable of telling us, through its own inner
rhythms, something about the larger rhythms of which it is
a replica."[3] It is as though our spiritual receivers, when we
turn the dials, find themselves in tune with a Divine center
in the universe from which pour into our hearts the messages of hope and faith that have inspired men since first
they felt the presence in the universe of a greater Spirit
than their own. God is the final value, in which all others
are centered and conserved.

If there were not something in the universe that draws
us, as the moon draws the sea, man's high aspirations
would have no meaning. Tides prove the moon is *there,*
even though clouds may cover it. This spiritual attraction
is more than passive orientation, for man actively *seeks* for
something by which he can realize the possibilities latent
in him. He has a tremendous capacity for dedication. He
is spiritually inflammable and takes fire from many things
—books, ideas and especially men who stir his heart. These
unloose power within him and profoundly influence what
he is and does. History is crammed with instances of men
lifted out of themselves by something quite beyond them.
Here seems to be no hypothetical First Cause ponderously
at work, but the dynamic influence of a lofty aspiration; the
practical effect, in a man's life, of his urgent pursuit of

---

[3] "The Enigma of Human Nature," *Main Currents in Modern
Thought,* September, 1956.

something like himself but infinitely greater. These seekings are in harmony with religion's belief that something exists which draws men toward itself so powerfully that nothing else becomes important to them. Aspiration is an expression of something deeper than intellect; a profound certainty that beyond man's body and beyond his mind there is a spiritual content in the universe with which his own spirit can from time to time communicate and from which he can draw strength and comfort. That this sense of Presence, this central, orienting core of things, is what we mean by God seems to me the clearest statement about Him we can make. No proof is here that He exists, but these facts do not contradict that great hypothesis, and for most men are the strongest objective evidence for its truth. This suggestion helps illuminate man's strange aspirations, which otherwise are so hard to understand, and gives them interpretation and significance. Something transcendent in the universe he needs and seeks. The rational and the moral are incomplete without the Divine.

There is another aspect of this problem of God's existence that deserves a place in our discussion. It is the certainty, shared by hosts of men and women through the ages, that from time to time, though usually for brief periods, they have had a vivid feeling of direct communication with a spiritual Being, something that seemed far higher than themselves and which, in the profound conviction of many, must be God Himself. This mystic sense of the Divine has been the seed of the church, a buttress of religious faith for those who have experienced it, and a proof for them that direct revelation of God is both possible and actual. If there is one word, however, that raises the hackles of an agnostic more than "purpose" does, it is "mysticism." This seems to him the very height of superstitious folly and obscurantism, the direct antithesis of the intellectual approach to truth that science cultivates. The chief quarrel he has with religion is that it practices, or at least condones, the mystical means of seeking for the truth.

Mysticism has its roots in the sense of mystery that man has always felt about his world. Much of this has come from the *unknown* element in his environment. Over the years its area has steadily been decreasing. That this will continue until *nothing* remains outside human knowledge is not to be expected. The greatest mysteries are ones we know exist but seem beyond the power of intellect alone to resolve—the origin and destiny of the universe, the nature of space and time, the character of life and its relation to matter and to man, and the dependence of mind and matter on each other. Before these, an attitude of wonder and of reverence, so out of fashion in these days of certainty, can hardly be avoided.

Most religions today have less to do than formerly with mystical experience, perhaps because such events are relatively rare or because of the general reaction against anything that savors of superstition. Prayer is practiced still, but one hears less about unmistakable spiritual revealings. It is significant, however, that in recent years a number of psychologists have examined the occurrence of such phenomena in a wide range of people and find that among a not inconsiderable number these experiences are rather frequent, manifest not only in men who are professedly religious but in those who have nothing to do with formal religion or are actually hostile to it. Maslow calls these manifestations "peak" experiences, and comes to the (to him) surprising conclusion that they are essentially like those which religion has long called spiritual ones. This field is attracting much attention now because of the fact that several so-called psychedelic substances have been found to induce mystical states in certain people which are indistinguishable from "natural" ones. They make possible an experimental study of mysticism. As is well known, the mystical element in Eastern religions is much greater than in the West. The significance of this fact for our problem has recently been emphasized by Professor Clark, who has said that by studying mysticism "we may come in contact with the psychological elements that underlie all religion and in this way may build a bridge of understanding between East and West."[4]

For a discussion of mysticism there is still nothing better than that classic by William James, *The Varieties of Religious Experience*. James documents generously his description of these experiences and, with the insight of a great philosopher and one broadly sympathetic to all aspects of man's nature, he considers their bearing on the fundamental problems of philosophy and religion, particularly as to what conclusions can be drawn about their reliability as indicators of religious truth. James regards such experiences seriously, and suggests, as now have many others, that it is through the unconscious mind that contact is made with something beyond ordinary perception. Dis-

---

[4] Walter Houston Clark, "The Mystical Consciousness and World Understanding," *Journal for the Scientific Study of Religion*, IV (Spring, 1965), 152–62.

cussing man's higher nature, he says: "He becomes conscious that this higher part is conterminous and continuous with a *more* of the same quality, which is operative in the universe outside of him, and which he can keep in working touch with, and in a fashion get on board of and save himself when all his lower being has gone to pieces in the wreck."[5]

To be sure, science has been able to contribute yet but little to an understanding of mystical phenomena, but they have now become a legitimate field for psychological investigation. One is justified, I believe, in agreeing, at least in part, with Maslow that "new developments in psychology are forcing a profound change in our philosophy of science, a change so extensive that we may be able to accept the basic religious questions as a proper part of the jurisdiction of science, once science is broadened and redefined."[6] Such conclusions are radically different from those of most psychologists today, but in time they may have an important influence on that fundamental difference between materialism and religion that involves the existence of God and man's relation to Him.

Whatever one may think of these cases of mystical experience, he should recognize that *experience,* of one sort or another, is the essence of religion, and that doctrines and theories are only *about* these experiences. Such experiences are a part of all spiritual sensitivity. They are most evident in those who have an acute appreciation of beauty

---

[5] *The Varieties of Religious Experience,* 1911, p. 508.

[6] Abraham H. Maslow, *Religions, Values, and Peak-experiences,* 1964, p. 11.

and of the delights of nature in her many forms. Such fortunate folk are often transported for a little while beyond the bounds of time and place into another region altogether. They have

> a sense sublime
> Of something far more deeply interfused,
> Whose dwelling is the light of setting suns,
> And the round ocean, and the living air,
> And the blue sky, and in the mind of man.[7]

These experiences are a source of pure delight. They are less extreme than those commonly called mystical, but if one has significance for the life of man, so, I think, does the other. Both are manifestations of the human spirit. Both, of course, can be written off as hallucinations, mere results of molecular activity in the brain and nothing more, but this makes meaningless a large and vivid part of human life, which to many is the most precious one of all. Both may point to something real in the universe that is deeper than material events; something to which the human spirit can respond and in which it feels at home. For many, such experiences are the essence of religion, true *revelations* of religious truth. Rational evidence certainly has an important part in religious conviction, but the life of faith begins with inner experience and is continually nourished by it. The primary basis of religion, as of aesthetics, is spiritual, not intellectual.

If, for one reason or another, most men should become convinced of the existence of a supreme Spirit in the uni-

---

[7] William Wordsworth, "Lines Composed Above Tintern Abbey."

verse, this would go far toward bringing them together in a common philosophy and brotherhood. Without this, I think, a common faith will be impossible. Where most difficulty in attaining this is to be found is in reaching an agreement about what God is like, about His "attributes," as the word is. If He is both omnipotent and good, how can these two qualities be reconciled? Over the relation between them hovers the ancient problem of evil. Men through the centuries have asked why, if God is really good and can really bring to pass the things He will, does He allow the hideous pain that man endures, and especially the undeserved suffering of innocence? The facile answers of theology give little comfort to one who feels "the bludgeoning of chance." Perhaps we still are paying thus for Adam's sin. Perhaps we would not value good had we no experience of evil. Perhaps suffering may be the necessary penalty our spirits pay for being locked within the bonds of matter. Perhaps we must accept it like a stoic, taking what comfort we can gather from the Book of Job. These suggestions yield but little solace to most men. Here the materialist, however, is at a disadvantage, for the man of faith whose heart is lighted by an inner flame has the certainty "that somehow good will be the final goal of ill," a consolation which he cannot justify by rational argument but which, in his very bones, he feels so sure of that he requires no proof.

Natural and Supernatural

Any discussion of a spirit that one may call Divine poses a problem that lies at the foundation of the opposition between the two philosophies we have been pondering—

the difference between the natural and the supernatural. Is the human spirit something that may be included among phenomena within the range of rational comprehension and that can be interpreted under the familiar concepts of the sciences, or does it bring in something quite outside all this and impossible of access by intellect alone? To most people the essential difference between the philosophies of materialism (naturalism) and those that are religious is that the primary concern of the latter is indeed with something beyond nature, something entirely repudiated by the former. Unless this ancient controversy can be resolved, the possibility that the two opposed philosophies will ever come together in any fashion meaningful for both is very slight.

Little new can be said about the supernatural today. For many years, and particularly since the rise of modern science four centuries ago, it has been the major target for those who accept nothing as true that cannot be validated by the senses and the intellect. The more dramatic examples of what were claimed to be supernatural were ghosts, spirit visitations and the work of mediums. Most of the investigations of our societies for psychical research have been concerned with happenings believed by some to be thus supernatural in origin. Religion now tends to dissociate its teachings from such things. Nevertheless, even in the enlightened religions of today there is clearly an essential element that is supernatural in the usual sense of the word. It is this element that is denied so vigorously by those who believe that religion not only is untrue but actually hinders an understanding of what truth is. Just as "superstition" is held in contempt by them as an attitude unworthy of enlightened men, so the "supernatural," a term often linked with it, is equally condemned. How, we are asked, can any intelligent person, in this age of science, give credence to a thing as tenuous and incomprehensible as spirit, in whatever guise it may be presented?

In the evolution of man's understanding, what were apparently supernatural happenings have so often later been explained by natural means that the conclusion may seem justified that everything will ultimately be understood without recourse to anything more. In his earlier years man invoked spirits to account for mysterious events, for whatever he could not otherwise explain. There is much, of course, that as yet we do not understand; but many scientists, with the splendid record of accomplishment behind them, believe that they finally will be able to explain everything that is *natural,* and that what is *super*natural can be disregarded since it is really nonexistent. The core of our problem, many philosophers would say, is not so much the opposition between materialism and religion as that between naturalism and supernaturalism. Is there any way by which these two so different attempts to reach the truth can now be reconciled? The essential issue, it seems to me, is whether what we have called the human spirit and, on a higher level, the Divine Spirit, actually and effectually *exist* or whether they are simply products of man's imagination; wish-fulfillments conjured up by a being who is lost and lonesome in the mysteries of the universe and seeks desperately somewhere for assurance.

One method of attacking the problem is through the activity of mediums, clairvoyants and so-called sensitives of various sorts. Many of these have proved to be charlatans, but evidence from others is not unimpressive, and only a dogmatist would make a blanket denial of the truth of all of them. Such a field as parapsychology, for instance, fails to find acceptance in the minds of many not so much because of lack of evidence as because there is no niche in the ideology of science into which it can be fitted. As a source of spiritual understanding, however, and a knowledge of God and of life beyond the grave, paranormal communications have been singularly devoid of interest or enlightenment. Their influence on religious thinking has been slight.

There is, I believe, a more hopeful way of approaching the supernatural—through science itself. As men push out more deeply into the unknown they accumulate an ever-increasing mass of facts about the universe, a mass that now has grown so huge that a finite mind can comprehend but a tiny segment of it. Most of these facts are of the familiar kind but more and more, especially in the physical sciences, they seem to make concepts necessary that are very different from the ones long looked upon as fundamental (see page 75). The theory of relativity, for example, requires that we regard space as curved, that the length of an object decreases as speed of its motion increases, that the highest speed possible is that of light, and that this never varies. There is good evidence that both the position and the momentum of a particle cannot be measured at the same time, and that an electron may be in two places at once. These facts certainly are not "natural" in the sense that we would expect them to be true, or that we can explain them by common sense. They do not fit into our ordinary conception of the way the universe is put together. We do not call them supernatural, however, presumably because they are based on facts that have been scientifically determined. We should put into the same class, perhaps, the still unexplained facts as to biological organization and other problems about life. We may finally have to accept all these as basic categories, following the lead of Bohr and Henderson, and learn to bring our other concepts into harmony with them. The presence in nature of such an unexplained—perhaps unexplainable—body of phenomena is not very far from the concept of the supernatural. At least it makes us wonder whether the term "natural" does not cover a much wider area than we have usually thought.

Let us not believe that we have found the last of these scientific phenomena that do not fit into a familiar framework of ideas, or that science has reached the limit of its concepts about the universe. Not only new facts but new principles are doubtless waiting to be recognized. In biology, much more complex than the physical sciences, revolutionary ideas have been slower to appear. Surely there are many other discoveries yet to be made here, not simply in the physics and chemistry of protoplasm, not simply in our ability to manipulate living things to our own ends, but in knowledge of what we may call the grand strategy of the organism. I believe that the life sciences are on the threshold of their greatest advance, that radical changes such as those that revolutionized physics half a century ago will have their counterparts here before long, and that discovery will lead us across new frontiers and into territories that we never knew existed.

And as for man, who can say how far the veil may be

torn away from our present view of his nature, about which we are now so complacently ignorant? Physics and chemistry and biology are all involved in him, but also something deeper still, the possibilities in protoplasm when it is free to express them in the highest product of the evolutionary process. If we are astonished at what has happened in physics since the century's turn, how much more so would we be, I am sure, if we could foresee the state of the sciences of man a hundred years from now. In that day, given a continuance of the acceleration that intellectual advance is undergoing, many answers to problems seemingly insoluble will be found, and ideas that now appear beyond the bounds of reason may come to take their seats in the house of ideological respectability. This does not mean that the gap between the natural and the supernatural will soon be closed but that these two aspects of the universe will come nearer together. Even mysticism, so often denied and derided, may come to have a rational interpretation. Truth is a far more complicated matter than in the simpler days of black-and-white materialism in the nineteenth century. There are few certainties left today on which we safely can rely, fewer self-evident axioms. Science is drawing closer to philosophy and to ultimate problems, where the evidence cannot be weighed on a chemical balance or measured by a micrometer scale. Physics has shown that matter, reality and freedom are not so easily defined and understood as once we thought they were. Biology, in the minds of its practitioners so confidently materialistic, will before many years, I think, begin to seek for deeper meanings in a living organism than a series of chemical reactions.

The attempts made in these pages to interpret the manifestations of the human mind and spirit in terms that are basically biological may ultimately prove fruitless, and the relation between biology and theology unconvincing. That religion is intimately concerned with life, however, cannot be denied; not only with life in a broad and figurative sense but life as one finds it in actual living organisms. It is toward the sort of encounter with philosophy and religion here suggested that the sciences of life are moving.

The humanist puts his faith in man alone, and for the atheist God does not exist. Not a few greet the mention of His name today with a derisive smile for "good old God." Many who are exemplary in life and keen of mind have become so certain He does not exist that they never think about Him any more. Nevertheless, as was said at the beginning of these discussions, any faith that leaves out the Divine cannot hope to become the universal one we seek. If this end of our bridge is not securely anchored, it cannot bear the weight of all mankind.

IX

SOME CONCLUSIONS

The Common Foundation

As THESE DISCUSSIONS draw now toward an end, it must be asked if they have contributed in any measure toward accomplishing the great task undertaken when they were begun—to frame a life philosophy that all men might be willing to support, that would be a means of bringing into harmony their many faiths, and that would help to join them more closely in a common brotherhood. Such a philosophy can be built, if at all, only by appealing to man's highest aspirations. Not through philosophy alone, or only by the concepts of religion, or by ideas from the sciences can this be successfully accomplished. Men are concerned most intimately with some aspect of the processes of *living;* with feeling, wanting, enjoying; with love, hate, hope, anxiety, despair and the other emotions that throng their hearts. These are all aspects of living organisms, not machines. Any philosophy that will attract all men must therefore deal with problems growing out of such biological facts rather than with purely physical ones.

Only on the basis of a common heritage as living things can men's philosophical unity be won. For this unity I have attempted to lay a foundation in the essential facts of biology. Briefly stated, the basis for agreement here proposed suggests that it should comprise the following conclusions:

We must discover how the material portions of the universe are related to the great imponderables in man called mind, soul and spirit. These come together in the transcendent fact of *life,* the bridge that connects the physical and the psychical. The system in which life is manifest is the *organism.* Its parts and processes are correlated by that paramount quality of life, *biological organization.* This has two major aspects. It integrates living stuff into *individuals,* from which the *self* and its attributes arise; and it regulates both development and behavior in conformity to *goals* that are set up in the organism. This is the germ of the directiveness or end-seeking so characteristic of all life activities. Desire and purpose are the conscious *experiences* of this directiveness and thus the basis of psychical life and the simplest acts of *mind.* The triumphs of man's intellect have their ultimate roots in biological goal-seeking.

Desires, fears, anxieties and other emotions result from the directiveness of man's life toward certain kinds of acts and qualities. The highest of these are his *ideals* or *values,* notably beauty, goodness, love and truth, which are the basis of his moral life and the aspirations of his *spirit.* These are hard to understand as the results of natural selection and random evolutionary change but seem, instead, to be the supreme development of tendencies latent in living stuff and coming to their highest expression in man. They are his attempts to attain harmony with something in the universe of which his own spirit is a part, a greater Spirit he calls *God*. These somewhat technical concepts of biology suggest how the spiritual side of man's nature, and thus the basis of his religion, is intimately related to his physical processes as an organism. They provide, I believe, a basis in the character of life for bringing into harmony the quantitative and material in man with what is imponderable and immaterial.

Around this nucleus of ideas as to the various aspects of man and his relation to the universe there may be laid a foundation for the unity we seek. Beliefs held in common are the cement of society. A bridge from matter to spirit can be built, I think, that will be somewhat different for different people but will still be able to carry the philosophical traffic of mankind. If all men could agree on the general interpretations that have been presented in these pages as to nature, life and man, we should not be far from the basic unity we seek. Many theologians and men of faith would be willing to accept these propositions now, and could build upon them the framework of a satisfying religion. They provide the possibility, I believe, for an ultimate coming together of our widely separated creeds. Materialists today would be less likely to accept them all for they include concepts long anathema to unbelievers. But if it should prove possible to interpret the material facts of life in such a way that these are consistent with a philosophy that is fundamentally, though perhaps not formally, religious—which is what I have been trying to accomplish in these discussions—then the way may be opened by which even one who calls himself a materialist, still maintaining much of his tough-mindedness, may be able to accept religion as an intellectually respectable avenue to truth. If increasing numbers of such men come finally to adopt this attitude, the days both of man's intellectual unity and of his moral and spiritual harmony, dreamed of for so long, will be in sight.

I have no illusions as to the vigor of the objections that will be thrown against these ideas by agnostics and by many supporters of religious and of biological orthodoxy. The suggestion that life is potentially a spiritual phenomenon is opposed to the prevalent view that it is only a biochemical process and that man is thus a chemical machine, a manifestation of nothing more subtle than the activity of DNA. The further idea that he has a specific nature of his own, expressed in an innate preference for certain values, savors too much of Providence to appeal to those who prefer a universe with no directiveness save the cold, impersonal effectuation of natural law. The many who regard these issues as already settled in favor of materialism will accuse me here of trying to fight a battle that long ago was lost.

The agnostic is fond of saying that his philosophy deals with facts alone, not nebulous and mystical theories; but let us remember that there are many facts other than those he recognizes which must also find interpretation in our philosophy. One such fact is the organism. Despite the recent great progress in biology, we are still as far as ever from understanding what produces and controls it. Another fact is the relation between matter and thought. These are certainly connected, but just how one influences the other we have not yet discovered. A third is the general unanimity among men as to their high values. The attempts to explain these values in evolutionary terms alone is unconvincing.

The assumptions of the materialist are attractive because they are simple and give a feeling that we understand how the universe is put together. They are in harmony with modern man's mechanistic ideas. But let us recognize that other assumptions may be equally valid. The stubborn facts just mentioned must somehow be brought into harmony with any philosophy worthy of our support. A system of belief that will appeal to most people is one which takes into account *all* the facts and gives the most plausible interpretation of them. The suggestions here presented merit consideration, I think, by those who sincerely wish to find a way to solve the difficulties with which man is now confronted. Some theologians and some men of science, who are sure they possess the only direct avenue to truth, will have little interest in such ideas, but men of open and more humble minds may find here something worth further exploration. Truth is vast, and the ideas that we accept today will doubtless be refined and modified as the years pass. In our search for unity let us set up no limits to this growth but keep our minds wide open to new understanding.

A Philosophy for the Individual

These conclusions should be useful not only in laying the foundation for a common human faith but in the related task of building a satisfying *personal* philosophy. A major question of our time is whether man has the moral fiber and the spiritual idealism required to maintain a highly organized society. Technology will provide the means by which man's intellect will have access to a still more vast array of facts and thus can bring the resources of the mind to the control of human behavior. The consequences may be fortunate or unfortunate for man. Not from his intellect, however, do his chief perils come today but from that deeper part of him whence rise his loves and hates, desires and passions, ideals and attitudes; the place where the best and worst of him are intermingled. Between the animal and the godlike here a momentous battle has for centuries been surging to and fro. Unless the better part of him is finally victorious, the penalty will not be simply the collapse of a kingdom or the downfall of a way of life but the destruction of civilization and even of mankind. The issue does not hang alone on the acceptance of a common faith but on how sincerely and effectively this faith is implemented in our behavior as *individuals*.

The central thesis of these pages is that life in essence is a seeking and a desiring; that the normative element in man, evident in bodily development and growing into his conscious desires and purposes, leads finally to his pursuit of values. One may not accept the biological interpretation of these matters that has been presented here but he will, I hope, agree with the conclusion as to personal philosophy that I should like to draw from them. It is, in brief, that what a person *wants* is for him the most important thing, for it determines his philosophy of life. What we are and do is governed primarily not by what drives us on, as psychology often maintains, but by our *ideals, our values*. A civilization can be judged by what its people seek. This in no small measure still, of course, is what man wanted in his jungle days, the satisfaction of many physical desires and needs. These, as we have seen, came actively into conflict with higher goals emerging in him as he became a man. The Good Life is one in which we seek the goals that the experience of the race has found to be most satisfying; goals that are *right,* in which desire conforms to obligation.

Human progress will not depend primarily on education and the advance of knowledge, as has so often been assumed. Much of the optimism of the Enlightenment seems now a bit naïve. Plato was only partly right when he said that if a man knows what is right, he will do it. Often he will not! It is more important that he should *want* to do what he *ought* to do, and that his ideals should be lofty. Idealism is the basis of a successful civilization, and idealism has a sound biological foundation. Many factors are involved in determining what a person's goals shall be. Some are built into the very chemistry of his cells. Some are determined by the culture pattern in which he happened to be reared. Others result from individual experience. Many are responses to the impulses of his own self-interest. But there is another and the most important factor of all, I believe—man's own decision. All organisms are goal-seekers but man alone, because of his capacity to imagine and create, is able to determine, at least to some degree, *what* goals to seek. This is a priceless gift, for he not only can choose what seem to him the highest ones but can raise them even higher by increasing his own sensitivity to them. The way to reach a satisfying personal philosophy is to find one's loftiest ideals and lift his life up to them.

Values are not fixed and unchanging but are modified as

culture and environment are altered and the pendulum of man's advance swings to and fro. Judgments of value are the most difficult ones to make, and in the changing texture of our lives it is by no means always certain what we *ought* to want. A man's chief responsibility, it seems to me, is to guard his values and ideals; not always to maintain them without alteration but to make sure that they are in harmony with the tested experience of our race and the whispered voice of the spirit in his heart. Carl Schurz once said: "Ideals are like stars; you will not succeed in touching them with your hands. But like the seafaring man on the desert of waters, you choose them as your guides, and following them you will reach your destiny."[1] The importance of this for our day is emphasized by the fact that many people are desperately groping for ideals that they have lost and without which their lives have no direction.

In the world today, and perhaps in any day, goodness— essentially unselfishness and love—is the most difficult goal to reach, for to eradicate selfishness one must overcome something deeply embedded in human nature. Men can learn to love beauty and truth far more easily than to love their brothers. Only when our spirits are warmed toward our fellows will true human unity be possible. The Golden Rule and the two great Commandments have little authority over many men today, but unless they are followed —under whatever auspices—the great experiment of civilization will not succeed. They provide the goals man's life must seek if it is to be lifted above the doubts and dangers and disasters of our time.

---

[1] Carl Schurz, Address at Boston, April 18, 1859.

Freedom

The attempt made in these pages to build a bridge from matter to spirit by way of the living organism and thus to make possible a reconciliation between the two camps into which mankind is now divided has other implications.

First, these conclusions suggest what the essential character of a human being really is. An organism can be described in physical terms, but this does not touch its real distinction. What binds it together as a unity, as we have seen, is the successive series of goals in conformity to which its structure and behavior are regulated. In man, the self is the sum of all the goals of the individual, all his purposes, desires and aspirations, the totality of his organizing relations. Mental life is not a "stream of consciousness," as it has sometimes been described, but rather a stream of *purposes*. In a very real sense, we *are* what we *want*. These wants are sometimes complex and fast-changing, as the norms within our nervous systems are altered when the environment is modified. Wants and desires express themselves in behavior. Thus in a man there is "an organic identification between what he *is* and what he *does,*" as Dr. Anshen has said in her Introduction. It is organic in the sense that being, wanting and doing are all aspects of the same biological process. In this fact lies the real unity of matter and spirit in man.

We may carry this idea further and apply it to the ancient problem of "freedom of the will." No other issue, says Professor Gordon Allport, causes such consternation for the psychologist today. The basic assumption of science is that the uniformity of nature is complete, the rule of natural law unbroken. And yet what gives significance to a man's life is that *he* and not some principle of mechanics seems to determine what he does. Freedom cannot be demonstrated by argument. It must be *experienced*. Nothing is more sure than a normal man's ability to stand and walk, if he *wants* to. If science denies this, we are inclined to think that its laws are not yet well enough understood. Human responsibility has no meaning without freedom. But the human *will* is something almost never mentioned nowadays since nobody sees how such a thing can really be effective. It is so impossible to reconcile freedom with determinism that many philosophers seem to want to forget the whole issue, and agree with Sherrington that "the important thing is less that man's will should be free than that man should think that it is free." This is simply surrender and an admission of impotence. The problem is too serious to abandon all attempts to solve it. If we are but puppets on a stage, and if what seem enterprises of such pith and moment, such noble causes into which men throw their lives, are nothing more at last than the running of a motion-picture film where everything that happens is inevitable and where the actors, despite their apparent labors, tragedies and satisfactions are as unreal as a dream—then the very bottom drops out of life and all our arguments are shadow-boxing.

The philosophy of determinism leaves many vital facts quite unexplained. Pain, as we have seen (see page 181), is advantageous for us as a warning of danger, and certainly implies freedom to avoid it. If we lack this freedom, the universe is a cruel place indeed; and if feelings of indecision, anxiety, regret, remorse and fear, which often make life miserable, are merely inevitable by-products of metabolism, life is quite meaningless.

But, granting the force of these arguments against determinism, how can we reconcile freedom with the uniformity of nature, the great requirement of science? *Something* certainly determines what we do. Psychologists believe it is our environment; geneticists, our genes, but they agree that *we* have nothing much to say about it. Perhaps something has been left out of our calculations here—consideration of what *we* really are. If it is true, as has just been suggested, that we are what we want, and what we want is what we do, then we are the means by which purpose is translated into deed. Purpose and purposer are one, and both are aspects of the regulatory power of living stuff that moves to the consummation of its purposes. Purpose is not something alien to the deed, something that is "free" or not. In a sense it *is* the deed. There is no *compulsion* here to act, for the very act is an expression of the self. Freedom is the coincidence between ourselves and our acts. Of course there are outer compulsions that bind us and prevent our doing many things we want to do. Though our wills are free, we cannot always bring to pass the things we will.

Does this seem too simple an answer for a problem that has long defied solution? Perhaps it is, but the concept of the self as the sum of all the individual's desires and purposes may be an idea of some importance in the problem of freedom. Behind all this, of course, is the question of what sets up these norms in the living stuff of the nervous system. This is the core of the problem of freedom. All that can be said at present is that we seem to have this power, and that what we do is an expression, in part, at least, of something innate in us, an expression neither entirely of our body chemistry nor of our environment, but of an inner directiveness or creativeness in us, related to our faculty of imagination, and basically a biological process.

These philosophical suggestions affect our ideas as to man's place in nature. Is he a stranger there, an alien, who has no relation at all to the material universe, a spiritual interloper? Or is he a creature whose psychical portion is one aspect of the physical; a being who is truly at home in nature? The latter view is more in harmony with the suggestions offered here. This question has repercussions even in literature. In recent years, for example, it has been the fashion to regard "nature poetry," such as Wordsworth's, as basically false since nature is purely material and thus can have no intimate relation to man. If the physical and the psychical are aspects of the same process in a living, material system, our ideas of matter as lifeless and inert should be revised. It is part of us and we of it. "Make friends with matter," said Emerson, "which the chatter of the schools would teach us to despise." An atom is far more than a little pellet of dead stuff. It is a group of positive and negative electrical charges and so has become, to our eyes, almost an ethereal thing. Since life has a material foundation, man himself is among the potentialities that matter holds. If this be so, matter is far more than a concourse of electrical charges, and should be relieved of the stigma imposed on it by an oversimplified philosophy. The organizing and pattern-making qualities of the universe, of which man's mind and spirit are the supreme examples, take their rise in matter, which may thus be looked on not as the dregs and debris of the universe but as the germ from which its higher qualities have come. From this viewpoint, a mature materialism may perhaps be looked on as ultimately a spiritual philosophy!

The Future

Another philosophical advantage in the concept that man, like all living things, is basically a goal-seeker is that it makes clear his continual involvement with the *future*. This, not the past, is the direction to which we are chiefly oriented. We have come through the past, indeed, but save as historians or antiquarians or evolutionists we pay scant heed to it. Man's preoccupation with the future is one of the most significant things about him. He is not only being; he is continually *becoming*. Everybody is going somewhere, and we can learn more about a person by finding what his destination is than by learning where he is now or whence he came. In psychology, Brentano's nineteenth-century emphasis on *intention,* though not popular today, agrees closely with the ideas presented here, for intention is but another name for purpose or goal. Emphasis on the future is also in harmony with the facts of physics, for entropy increases, and time's arrow points ahead. "Human nature," says Dr. Anshen, "loses its most precious quality when it is robbed of its sense of things beyond, unexplored and yet insistent."

Man has ever been eager to discover what will happen in the time to come. The unknown future tantalizes him. To lift the veil that covers it has ever been what he has most eagerly desired. Prophets, not chroniclers, are the men he heeds most closely. The great oracles of classical times had a profound influence on his life, and for sibylline books he always has been willing to pay fabulous sums. Even today, the future of the universe engages man's deep interest. To extrapolate it from the past is very difficult, and most students of evolution, cosmic or biological, deny that any trends are visible. Teilhard de Chardin, however, with the courage characteristic of him, has postulated what he calls the Omega Point, the end toward which all moves, and supports this profound idea with various arguments.

Man's concern with the future is sharpest when he considers his individual life as it rolls onward with the wheel of time. Whence he comes indeed is interesting, but whither he is going when his mortal life is done has always been the question he most wants to answer. Man, alone among all living things, knows that he must die. As he sees his friends pass, one by one, into the state that he calls death, he wonders what has happened to them and what fate has in store for *him*. Here at last the goals he has sought all his life to gain seem finally to elude him; the roads he so long has followed run out to their end.

In this dark mystery of death, what has the philosophy of life to offer for man's consolation? That life for us, in anything like the form we know it here, will continue beyond the grave seems so inherently improbable that many have quite abandoned hope of it. But at least we know today that death is not everywhere a necessary evil. Simple animals and plants are able to continue life indefinitely. "The immortality of the Protozoa" when conditions are favorable states this vividly. Cells can live indefinitely in tissue culture. There is a cogent biological reason, however, why death should almost invariably occur. Without it, evolutionary progress would have been impossible, for the earth would have become so cluttered with "old models" that there would have been no room for new and better ones. The habit of dying was probably a result of natural selection, since those species that could thus get rid of older types would have an advantage in competition since they could produce better adapted ones more rapidly.

But for a man who faces death it is small consolation to know that the reason he must go is simply to make room for someone else. He may take comfort in the fact that his own biological stock, his very genes, will still live on in his descendants, or that he will have a sort of immortality in his contributions to human life that may survive him. He may also come to realize that man is not made for earthly immortality since this would lead at last to insufferable boredom. His concern for the future, of which we have been speaking, is not for something everlasting here on earth but rather for a place, always receding into the unknown, toward which his aspirations continually draw him, the endless goal of life's adventurous quest.

Here the theoretical physicist can make a contribution to the argument. If survival occurs, the problem of identity is important. Do we our*selves* live on? The individual, the self, implies a continuing identity. In terms of matter, however, identity has lost its meaning, for it is impossible to follow the course of an individual electron or an ultimate particle, since these things seem actually to go out of existence and come in again. What *does* persist, what *is* the basis of identity, is the *form* of the whole system. We are now used to the idea that matter is continually entering and leaving our bodies without changing *us*. The same thing is happening, in a sense, at the atomic level. All this magnifies the significance of the organizing formative pattern about which I here have said so much. A human being is a complex pattern that life makes in matter; something that persists even when its material is completely changed; a norm set up in living stuff to which the individual, in its development and behavior, conforms. This concept is the nearest that biology can come to that of the *soul* (see page 138). Such a norm is so ubiquitous and persistent that one may consider the possibility that it is the dominant element in the organism and, by governing the distribution of matter, actually *makes* the body, an idea quite opposite to the one we almost instinctively hold; and the more we consider how little we know of the real nature of that normative essence which is at the bottom of every organism, the less dogmatic we become about its role in life and the greater begins to appear the possibility that it may exist after the body it has formed has been destroyed, as a machine pattern can survive its products. The body wears out and finally dies, just as an old car wears out and can go no farther. From a human body nothing leaves at death; not matter, not energy. What is gone is simply an organizing pattern, something that maintains an individual's identity.

Every organism is creative and molds matter to its own normative design. Perhaps this creative faculty, especially in man, where it is developed to such a superlative degree, is part of the creativeness found in the universe as a whole and that I have suggested may be an attribute of Deity. If the creative, goal-seeking element in life partakes of God Himself, it would be strange if this partnership were to be dissolved at every death. If man's spirit is part of the great continuity of creation, this should redeem it from destruction and enable it to flow back into the creative reservoir from whence it came.

This deep problem philosophy has pondered long. One suggestion is that there are *two* orders in the universe—the familiar one of time, the *natural* order, the one of our common life; and, quite distinct from it, the *eternal* order, known to us only in mystical experience. For the mystic, these two intersect briefly and in those moments he lives in eternity. If the universe does have these two orders, the impossibility of reconciling them obviously prevents our understanding eternal things—such as immortality and God —in terms of the world of time. If we can come to accept this and see the impossibility of proving the truth of religious ideas by scientific evidence, we can have a meaningful relation with both orders and find a satisfactory place for both in our philosophy. This, I believe, is an important concept for the construction of the common faith we seek.

But these are philosophical arguments that carry little conviction to most men. What makes many still believe in some sort of endless life is that mortality does not make sense to them. It violates the great idea of evolutionary continuity to think that life should end while it is so incomplete. We have a feeling of tragic frustration, as though the curtain had come down at the end of the second act. As Whitman said, "If maggots and rats ended us, then Alarum! for we are betrayed!" To Darwin himself it was an intolerable thought that man and all other higher forms of life should be doomed to complete annihilation after such long, slow progress upward. There is something in us that rebels at such a fate.

But, rebel or not, as rational beings we must recognize that such a gloomy destination may indeed be the one to which the world is moving. This is what makes life, to many minds, so tragic, and has given birth to pessimistic philosophies like existentialism. It is the penalty that man must pay if he gives up a belief in God. Like the existence of the soul, the freedom of the will and the voice of conscience, immortality is one of those profound problems about which many men today profess to have lost interest, either because the problems are insoluble or because they seem meaningless. But we cannot escape them. They are *not* meaningless, and I believe they *can* be solved if we progress in understanding as far as we already have in knowledge. Our answers to them will determine what we are and what the world will be. They are a vital part of our great problem.

We must depend here not so much upon philosophers and men of science as on poets and other interpreters of the spirit. The problem of immortality is wrapped up in one stanza of "In Memoriam":

> The wish that of the living whole
> No life may fail beyond the grave,
> Derives it not from what we have
> The likest God within the soul?[2]

The Role of Christianity

The dominant religion in those parts of the world where modern science developed was Christianity, a Christianity

---

[2] Part LV, stanza 1.

intellectualized by Greek thought, organized by Rome's imperial tradition and modified in a hundred ways by climate, racial differences and pagan influences from the past. It is chiefly in this religion, long held together by Rome but much of it freed four centuries ago, that the battle between materialism and the concepts of religion now is being waged. What relation, we may ask, has Christianity to the problems we have been discussing?

In the history of this faith there are many dark and bloody pages. It has a long tradition of anti-intellectualism, and it holds, or has slowly retreated from, a series of positions that are quite indefensible in the light of modern knowledge. Its ecclesiastical organizations have often been harsh and tyrannical. In this secular age organized Christianity has a low repute among many who call themselves intellectuals. They ridicule such absurdities as the Scopes trial and the teachings of fundamentalism. And yet much of Christianity, gradually freeing itself from control by the unintelligentsia, shows a surprising toughness, and in each generation goes back to its sources from which still flow, unpolluted, what for many are the true waters of life. Christianity is not conquering the world today any more than it did in the Crusades, but there is in it something germinative and compelling. To compare it with other religions, as one among equals, is for many people sacrilegious, since they look upon it as unique, the True Faith, established by the Lord Himself; but such an argument has no weight with the great majority of mankind, who follow other systems of belief.

Christianity has some advantages over other faiths, however, as a means of universal service to mankind. The essence of it, its basic teaching and its root idea, is *love*.

Sometimes this has been very far from evident in the struggle between religious partisans; often it is choked by accretions of ritual and doctrine, but underneath everything, its heart still beats. Man's love for God, God's love for man, and, growing from these two, man's love for *man,* is the firm triangle on which a sound society is based. Love is broader than mere affection, for it involves altruism, unselfishness, the willingness to sacrifice one's own welfare for that of someone else. Men are very far indeed from this ideal today, but it commands their ultimate allegiance. Without the Golden Rule, a culture finally will fall apart. The common faith we seek cannot be reached until men approach the problem in the spirit of unselfishness and good will. It is hard to see how the world's salvation from the forces that now threaten it can be gained if this leaven is not actively at work within it. Material factors will ultimately prove powerless unless they supplement a spiritual factor, love itself. This is the essence of the Christian doctrine and a reason for its great service to mankind.

Another advantage of Christianity for the common faith we seek is in its central idea of revelation. This, too, is often held up to scorn, and certainly the old idea of verbal revelation is so naïve as to be of little meaning. But man continually seeks for revelations of many kinds, in science, philosophy, poetry and other fields. Often the veil is torn away and light pours in on ordinary men as ideas and inspirations that well deserve the name of revelation. But deeper still are those revealings that answer innate and heartfelt longings for enlightenment. Imagination delves below the level of direct experience and finds a deeper truth than the mind alone can know. Thus is it with the idea we have of God. Like space and time, He is infinite and cannot be grasped by sense or intellect. Jesus, however, was a material person who *could* be seen and heard and touched. By their physical senses the men and women of his day apprehended at least a part of what he was, and through his words we still can share this knowledge. Qualities we commonly attribute to Divinity were his, and our understanding of them is greatly aided by witnessing their personification in a living man. Regardless of how this is formulated in theological terms, the facts are there, and we can interpret them as we please. Only Christianity gives this vivid demonstration of what God is like.

In much of our Western world, Christianity occupies a preferred position as compared to other faiths. It provides a moral code so lofty that, if followed, it would produce an ideal society. More than any other faith, I think, it is in harmony with the philosophy that we have been proposing, and it has the universal quality necessary for the religious basis of such a philosophy. Its testing time, however, is coming when it must prove that it can keep pace intellectually with a changing world and at the same time provide the inspiration that has been its service in the past. Each of the other great religions also claims the allegiance of many sincere followers and has something to offer to the universal philosophy we seek. Contributions of the best from every source will add to its strength and make it attractive to a wider company than one that has its roots in a single religious interpretation alone.

The ancient writings do not tell us whether the men who raised the tower of Babel ever attempted to return and finish their uncompleted task. The site of the great tower is marked today by only a vast mound of rubble in the desert sands. Let us profit from the example of those ancient builders, to whose work confusion put an untimely end, and leave to those who follow us not the wreckage of a burned-out world but a thriving Tower of Hope, firmly held together by the bonding of a common faith. To build this faith is man's imperative task today. "Time driveth onward fast" into a future that is quite unknown. If we march toward it as an army, ranks closed around a common vision of the truth, our fate will be far more auspicious than if we meet it like a rabble with a thousand goals. Confusion once defeated us. Let us not yield to it again.

X

FURTHER PERSONAL REFLECTIONS

THE READER OF A book that deals with the profound problems this one faces deserves, I think, to know what are the opinions in these matters of the author himself and how he happened to acquire them. These questions I shall try to answer very briefly here.

Every man carries much of his childhood with him as he grows up. One's philosophy, like his tastes and his politics, is determined in no small measure by the environment in which he has been reared. This, I am sure, is true in my own case. Both my parents were native New Englanders, brought up in the Puritan tradition when this had lost its earlier austerity but not its sense of moral responsibility or its religious devotion. Our home was a Christian one. We read the Bible. We went to church. We kept the Sabbath, though with much less rigor than our forefathers had kept it. When I hear Christianity disparaged as hypocritical and meaningless, I remember with gratitude the affectionate selflessness and high ideals of my parents and the circle of our relatives and friends. Religion was not forced upon me but became a natural way of life. I have never abandoned

it, and today am an active member of the Congregational
Church. This fact will be explained by many as the result
of early conditioning which I have never been able to out-
grow and which necessarily so vitiates my conclusions that
they are of little worth. Others will be surprised that a man
of science should be naïve enough to be a sincere church-
man. I would urge such men to retreat a little from their
certainties and to recognize the possibility that some ideas
different from their own may perhaps be true.

Natural history always interested me, and as a boy I
collected plants and insects and developed a passion for
ornithology. In early years I began to think about the relations between the science of life and the problems of living.
My father, a lifelong teacher of the sciences, had been
a student of N. S. Shaler at Harvard and was a convinced
evolutionist. The difference between Darwin's explanation
of creation and that in the first chapter of Genesis never
troubled me, since the latter was so obviously allegorical,
and I therefore never had to undergo the agony of a violent
break between religious orthodoxy and scientific fact.

In my undergraduate years at Harvard, many things
were happening in the sciences. The revolution in physics
was taking place. Einstein's early publication on relativity
was beginning to attract attention. Modern genetics was
developing. The star of biochemistry was rising, and
Jacques Loeb had written *The Mechanistic Conception of
Life*. The implications of such works were that a living
thing is essentially a physicochemical machine, and that
if one could discover its ultimate physical basis he would
know everything about it. These new discoveries emphasized sharply the old mechanistic ideas about man's nature.

Quite different concepts were being expressed by others, notably William James, whose great book *The Varieties of Religious Experience* was published at about this time. This and other writings of James much impressed me, and the reader can perhaps see his influence in the present book.

I majored in botany in college, and my early scientific work was on the morphology and anatomy of the higher plants, which gave me an interest in organic form. This led to a concern with developmental problems, especially after a course on experimental embryology with Professor H. W. Rand, who introduced me to the work of Driesch and others in this field. Most of my own research has been on developmental and genetic problems in plants.

A student of development is confronted at every turn by an outstanding fact, the *organism*. A living thing is more than an aggregate of molecules and genes, of cells and tissues and organs. It is an integrated *whole* in which all the parts are closely related, both in structure and function. A series of regulatory processes maintains this unity and produces the orderly changes by which the adult develops from the egg. To account for these facts is very difficult. One circumstance about organic development has always seemed particularly significant to me: that as the egg grows into a particular kind of organism, this developmental process tends to proceed to its conclusion even though its normal course may be disturbed by accident or experiment. The *end* tends to be the same, whatever happens. Throughout development there seems to be immanent in the embryo an end—the mature organism—that will ultimately be reached. I have long been impressed by the resemblance between this process and another ultimately biological one—purposive behavior, the pursuit of ends or goals. The resemblance between these two has seemed to me to present the possibility of finding the relation between development and behavior and thus between the physical and the psychical aspects of man. It offers a biological foundation for what we commonly call the mental part of man. If in material activities can be found a basis for psychical processes, the way may open to break down the antithesis between these two basic aspects of man's nature. The integrative and goal-seeking character so evident in bodily development may help us interpret the integrative and goal-seeking character equally evident in psychological processes.

An invitation to give the McNair lectures at the University of North Carolina in 1948 gave me an opportunity to rethink this problem and present it more formally. These lectures were published in a small book.[1] I later extended the idea in two other volumes[2] to include various wider problems.

The suggestions in these books received the approval of a number of religious leaders but gained little support from biologists, although several students of the life sciences notably E. S. Russell, Ralph Lillie and W. E. Agar, had published conclusions somewhat similar to mine. In this idea, what repels those who are entrenched in biological orthodoxy is partly the use of the inflammatory word "purpose," a term that conjures up the old question of final

---

[1] *Cell and Psyche,* 1950.
[2] *The Biology of the Spirit,* 1955. *Matter, Mind and Man,* 1957.

causes and the effect of mind on matter, and partly the fact that I am introducing here support for something that is not material and therefore should not be discussed in scientific terms. For this I have often been called a vitalist and a mystic, both of whom are beyond the pale of biological respectability.

This idea of a relation between development and behavior, whether it is sound or not, seems hard for many people to understand. They tend to confuse purpose in an individual, which is what I have discussed, with *cosmic* purpose, a very different problem. Many also seem to think that the ends or goals of which I speak are necessarily favorable to the individual and that I am therefore attempting to explain adaptation as something that happens naturally. Nothing could be farther from the truth in both cases. I have had nothing to say about cosmic purpose, and agree entirely that adaptation is the result of natural selection.

What *is* involved in all this is the problem of biological organization, of what it is that makes an organism instead of a collection of molecules and genes. Modern biology has not yet come to grips sufficiently with this problem, and some biologists hardly recognize that it exists. My memory in these matters reaches back more than half a century, but I cannot see that during this time any significant progress toward its solution has been made. The recent discovery of the biochemistry of genes and the significance here of two of the nucleic acids is extremely important but it fails to touch the main problem. We have always tended to underestimate the complexity of living stuff. I believe that biology today is in much the same position that physics was before our understanding of relativity and quantum theory, and that new principles will in time be discovered that will illuminate our present ignorance. It is very important that we recognize this possibility and that we refrain from dogmatic certainties and the belief that the most important facts about life are already known.

The present belief of most biologists, supported by the highest pontifical authority in the science, that natural selection can explain all the important changes man has undergone, deals with only part of the story. His body and brain are doubtless the products of biological evolution, but what often is overlooked is that his most distinctive traits are of relatively recent appearance, having arisen during his so-called cultural evolution, and only to a minor degree could be the result of natural selection. These traits, particularly his devotion to certain higher values, tell us much about his real character and suggest that a knowledge of how it has developed involves problems beyond the scope of biochemistry or the selective process.

This conclusion, I am sure, will be greeted with complete dissent and even derision by the orthodox. I believe, however, that biologists and psychologists, in their justified reaction against the old idea that man was unique in his creation and his character, have failed to recognize how remarkably specific an organism he really is. Humanists, indeed, glorify him, but only as the paragon of animals. He seems to me far more than that. The heights and depths of his nature we have hardly yet begun to comprehend. His sensitivity to beauty and his power to create it; his courage; his devotion to his fellows; his willingness to sacrifice himself for others, and the profound faith that he has nourished through the generations that there is a spiritual core to things, are qualities I find very hard to account for as products of a "fortuitous concourse of atoms," or as the result of a competition to leave the most offspring. Their meaning must be a deeper one than this.

The portions of my personal credo, presented in such brief form here, have been discussed in more detail on earlier pages. They have served as a basis for the task which is the book's chief purpose—to help construct a foundation on which can be erected a philosophy of life acceptable to people of a wide variety of opinions and that perhaps may be a means of promoting human brotherhood and counteracting the divisive factors now so prevalent among men. It is my hope, perhaps a very forlorn one indeed, that the philosophy developed here will be persuasive enough to make some slight contribution to this, the most ambitious task a man could ever undertake.